TEA

TROPICAL AGRICULTURE SERIES

The Tropical Agriculture Series, of which this volume forms part, is a series of books on tropical agriculture which is being published under the editorship of D. Rhind, C.M.G., O.B.E., B.SC., F.L.S., F.I.BIOL.

Already published

Child, R. *Coconuts*

Grist, D. H. *Rice*

Harris, W. Victor *Termites*

Hickling, C. F. *Tropical Inland Fisheries*

Simmonds, N. W. *Bananas*

Smith, F. G. *Beekeeping in the Tropics*

Urquhart, D. H. *Cocoa*

Williamson, G. and Payne, W. J. A. *An Introduction to Animal Husbandry in the Tropics*

TEA

by

T. EDEN
D.Sc., F.R.I.C.

Formerly Director,
Tea Research Institute of
East Africa

SECOND EDITION

LONGMANS

LONGMANS, GREEN AND CO LTD
48 Grosvenor Street, London W.1
*Associated companies, branches and representatives
throughout the world*

*First published 1958
Second impression 1960
Second edition 1965*

PRINTED IN GREAT BRITAIN
BY WESTERN PRINTING SERVICES LTD BRISTOL

FOREWORD

by

SIR G. W. NYE, K.C.M.G., O.B.E.

Agricultural Adviser, Ministry of Overseas Development

DR. EDEN's book is a very welcome addition to the Tropical Agricultural Series of books published with the encouragement of the Colonial Advisory Council of Agriculture, Animal Health and Forestry. An authoritative book on tea covering both field and factory operations has been badly needed for a long time; the need has recently become acute because of the efforts which are being made both to expand existing tea industries and also to develop new ones in potentially promising areas. The tea industry of East and Central Africa is being expanded by estates and recently in Kenya by African smallholders. This industry supplies not only domestic requirements, which at present absorb a large proportion of the production, but also export markets. Tea is being developed for local consumption and export in Mauritius, and a recent survey has drawn attention to the possibility of developing a tea industry in the Southern Cameroons where tea has already shown promise. A second reason for welcoming this book is its authoritative nature. After working at the Rothamsted Experimental Station Dr. Eden has had a long and distinguished career in tea, first with the Tea Research Institute of Ceylon and, more recently as Director of the Tea Research Institute of East Africa. It would be difficult to find anyone more fitted to write this book than Dr. Eden through his long and wide experience, his scientific, and what is equally important, practical approach to the many problems involved, and, not least, his clarity of style. Dr. Eden set himself the task of describing tea cultivation and manufacture and discussing the principles involved; he has fulfilled his task admirably and his book will be found valuable and stimulating to all who are concerned either with existing tea industries or with new developments and I have much pleasure in commending it to their notice.

PREFACE TO THE SECOND EDITION

TEA is an immemorial crop originally grown and manufactured by peasants in a very primitive manner. During the past century and a quarter it has been cultivated, in regions often far removed from its ancient home, by intensive methods that have transformed tea-growing and processing into a complicated industry. Mechanical means of cultivation, the use of fertilizers and power-driven machinery in factories of modern design have revolutionized in many respects the primitive technique, but the care of the individual bush and the harvesting of the crop still elude mass treatment. Tea cultivation is, in fact, a horticultural operation carried out on an agricultural and industrial scale.

My connection with tea cultivation in two contrasted regions, and my visits to other tea-growing areas in Asia and Africa have confirmed me in the belief that there is no single and exclusive way of growing tea well. This conviction has determined my approach to the method of writing this book. Three possibilities were open to me: (1) to write an account of the tea industry of an encyclopedic nature, ranging as far and wide as possible: (2) to write a manual of instruction, in other words a planting manual, based on the needs and experiences of a particular region, and (3) to give a descriptive account of the various stages of tea cultivation and manufacture on which to base a discussion of the principles involved. My choice has been this last, mainly because it has been my predominant interest, and partly because the other avenues of approach have already been adopted. I have tried to discuss the fundamental agricultural and technological principles of the existing industry so that they may have relevance wherever tea cultivation is carried on. In the course of so doing I have been only too well aware of the gaps in my knowledge of this fascinating crop.

I have tried to put at the disposal of the reader the conclusions derived from the considerable volume of research that has been devoted to the tea crop. Naturally the interpretation is coloured by my own experience, but I offer no excuses for this because the dullest of all books is that which conceals the viewpoint of the author.

vii

My choice of references has been consciously selective. I have generally chosen sources that gave the completest discussions and those that are most readily available for reference. The books and papers quoted themselves provide a wide range of cognate sources.

Since the first edition of this book was published there have been significant developments in scientific research devoted to tea culture and manufacture. Certain sections of the text have accordingly been recast in order to report and discuss them. The chapter on Shade and that providing the Statistical Review have been entirely rewritten. Greater attention has been given to the development of new techniques and new equipment for the manufacture of tea which aim at promoting a considerable degree of automation. Other revisions made necessary by new work are related to the following subjects: taxonomy; the fundamental chemistry of tea leaf; weed control; fertilizer efficiency; the pathology of pests and diseases and the improvement of planting material.

T.E.

Sidmouth
November 1964

ACKNOWLEDGEMENTS

EVERYONE with whom I have discussed the problems of the tea industry over a period of many years has, in a sense, made a contribution to this monograph. I am grateful to them all for their interest and criticism, which has helped me to clarify my own ideas.

In particular, I owe an inestimable debt to my former colleagues in the Tea Research Institutes of Ceylon and of East Africa, for the many lively discussions and conferences which have been to me so rewarding a feature of the close co-operation in which we worked.

Equally great is my debt to my wife who, in many ways, has facilitated the collection of material for, and the writing of, this book. In the midst of a busy life she has found time to take over completely the production of the manuscript and all the ancillary secretarial duties involved.

I am very grateful for various items of specialized help: to Mr. R. D. Morrison, Secretary, the International Tea Committee, for statistical data; to Miss M. Scott, Information Officer, the International Tea Market Expansion Board Ltd., for details of legislation relating to tea in Ceylon; to the Royal Netherlands Embassy, for information about Indonesian associations and research; to the Indian Tea Association and Dr. E. A. H. Roberts, for similar information relating to India; to Mr. H. D. Bradshaw for information about the London Tea Market; to the Government Chemist for details of procedure under the Customs and Excise Act; to the Commonwealth Institute of Entomology, the Commonwealth Mycological Institute and Dr. J. B. Goodey for help in nomenclature; to Mr. E. L. Keegel for allowing me to see his monograph on Tea Manufacture in Ceylon whilst it was still in proof; and to Mr. D. H. Boalch, Librarian, Rothamsted Experimental Station, for reading facilities in the library.

The permissions to reproduce photographs and diagrams are listed separately in detail. I have made such extensive use of photographs by Mr. G. Gamble, Provincial Agricultural Officer, Kenya, that it is a pleasure as well as a duty to acknowledge his ready help here.

Finally, I am most grateful for the constant help and consideration afforded me by the late Sir Harold Tempany, C.M.G., C.B.E., and Mr. D. Rhind, C.M.G., O.B.E., F.L.S., in their editorial capacities, and to Messrs. Longmans, Green & Co. Ltd., and their staff, for so patiently guiding me through the complexities of publication.

In the preparation of a second edition I am grateful for the further help from the International Tea Committee, the Tea Market Expansion Board, the Commonwealth Mycological Institute and the Commonwealth Institute of Entomology. The Directors of the Tea Research Institutes in Assam, Ceylon and East Africa have kindly included me in the mailing list of their publications. J. H. Thomas and Co., Private Ltd., of Calcutta, supplied statistics that were not available elsewhere.

For permission to reproduce photographs we are indebted to the following:

Mr. A. F. Beakbane for Plates 8, 14, 42, 52; Robert Capa, Magnum, for Colour Plate III; Messrs. Davidson & Co. Ltd. for Plates 55, 56, 59, 60; The East African Agriculture and Forest Research Organization for Plates 33, 34; Federal Information Department, Salisbury, S. Rhodesia, for Plate 5 (photograph by R. L. Kinsey); Mr. G. Gamble for Plates 2, 3, 7, 11, 12, 17, 19–24, 29–31, 51; Mr. F. Gill for Plate 13; the author and Messrs. W. Heffer & Sons Ltd. for Plates 46 and 47 from E. Hainsworth, *Tea Pests and Diseases and their Control*; the Indonesian Embassy for Plates 6, 18, 48, 50; the Kalivertriebstelle G.M.B.H. for Colour Plates IV, V; Messrs. Marshall, Sons & Co. Ltd. for Plates 53, 54, 58, 61; the Executors of the late T. Petch for Plates 36–9, 43–5, and Colour Plate VI from Petch, *Diseases of the Tea Bush*, Macmillan & Co. Ltd.; Pictorial Press for Plate 4; the Tea Bureau for Plates 9, 10, 26, 27, 49; Dr. Tubbs and the *J. hort. Sci.* for Plate 28; Aloy H. Perera for Colour Plates I and II.

Plates 40 and 41 are reproduced from *Colonial No. 292, Blister Blight Disease of Tea*, by permission of the Controller, H.M. Stationery Office.

Plates 1, 16, 25, 62, 63, 65–7 are Shell Photographs.

For permission to reproduce or redraw diagrams we are indebted to the following:

The Editor, *The Empire Journal of Experimental Agriculture* for Figs. 10 and 12; the Central Province Ceylon Tea Company for Fig. 21; the Indian Tea Association for Fig. 9; the Tea Bureau for Fig. 1; the Tea Research Institute of Ceylon for Figs. 4, 5, 7, 8, 14, 15, 16, 17, 18, 19, 20.

For permission to reproduce data published in *Tropical Agriculture* (Fig. 6) and *Outlook on Agriculture* (Fig. 11) my thanks are due to the Editors and to the Imperial College of Tropical Agriculture, and to Imperial Chemical Industries Ltd., respectively.

Fig. 2 is reproduced from Cobley, *Introduction to the Botany of Tropical Crops*, Longmans, and is based on an engraving lent by the Tea Bureau.

CONTENTS

LIST OF ILLUSTRATIONS

SOUTH-EAST ASIA

The extension of the industry in its modern form started in India. Between 1818 and 1834 several private individuals and government officials had interested themselves in the possibilities of tea cultivation in north-east India, primarily as a source of revenue, but also because relations with China, the sole source of the commodity for European trade, were disturbed, and from time to time normal trade was suspended. Claims were made that "wild tea" had been discovered in Nepal and the Manipur district. Representations were made to the Governor-General which resulted in the formation of a "Committee of Tea Culture" in 1834 consisting of "gentlemen of high character and great intelligence" in Calcutta. After experimenting at the Calcutta Botanic Gardens with a consignment of tea seed from China attention was turned to tea found growing in a "wild" state within the territory of the East India Company, from Sadiya to the borders of the Chinese province of Yunnan. The Chinese importations were discontinued and the future Indian enterprise was developed from these locally discovered types. From the start, the industry was built up on the basis of the limited liability company.[4, 5, 6]

In Ceylon the serious cultivation of tea began in the decade of the eighteen-seventies. There is a record of ten acres in 1867 and by 1880, 14,226 acres were reported.[7,8] In the next fifteen years expansion had reached the total of 305,000 acres, for, with governmental encouragement, tea was replacing coffee which was rapidly being devastated by the attacks of the Coffee Rust fungus. This spectacular enterprise was the work of individual proprietary planters and it was not until just before the First World War that the now prevalent company organization began to entrench itself. About 12 per cent of the acreage is however occupied by small holdings of less than 10 acres extent.

In Java, following an initial importation of seed from Japan in 1824, six journeys were made between 1827 and 1833 by a government envoy to collect seed and workmen from China. Tea cultivation was a government monopoly, and continued so until 1860. It was unremunerative and remained so until the introduction of Assam types in 1878. The foundation of tea culture in Sumatra was inaugurated in 1909 by a British firm. The tea industry in Indonesia suffered complete disorganization during the Second World War and the succeeding years of political and economic instability. Disregarding the small holdings which before the war contributed about 17 per cent of the total production, the destruction involved in uprooting or cutting down tea and growing subsistence crops has reduced the

Chapter I

THE DEVELOPMENT OF TEA CULTURE

Place of Origin—S.-E. Asia—Africa—Other Regions.

PLACE OF ORIGIN

THE tea plant, *Camellia sinensis* has been cultivated for so long that its home as a wild plant is a matter of speculation. Certainly in south-east China tea has been used as a beverage for between two and three thousand years, and nobody has ever claimed to have found wild tea in China proper.[1] From time to time assertions have been made that wild types have been found, but in all probability these plants, usually found in clusters, are relics of previous cultivation in the unrecorded past. Considering the localities in south-east Asia where various types of tea are now established, it is likely that they have been dispersed from a centre near to the source of the Irrawaddy and have been spread out fan-wise into south-east China, Indo-China and Assam. Moreover according to Kingdon Ward[2] it is probable that this locus was only a secondary one and that the indigenous species had its origin farther north. In support of this contention it is pointed out that, in the three areas mentioned, the greater part of the tea conforms to an individual type, but that in each place examples of one of the other types can be found.

Attempts have been made to claim for these types sub-specific rank. Watt definitely suggested four varieties, *viridis*, *bohea*, *stricta* and *lasio-calyx*, but later research tends to limit the description to the locality in which the types are most prevalent and to describe them as *assamica*, *sinensis*, and *cambodia* respectively. All these types hybridize freely.[3]

From the main centres of cultivation in south-east Asia tea has spread far and wide into tropical and subtropical areas whose broad characteristics correspond to regions of tropical rain forest, tropical savannah and summer rain. From being a traditional peasant cultivation in the Far East, tea culture has developed into an important plantation industry employing considerable capital and controlled at the present time mainly by limited liability companies of European origin.

1

1. A typical Kenya tea-field showing wind-breaks
and young dispersed shade trees of *Grevillea robusta*

2. Darjeeling tea on steep slopes

3. Pruned tea on single-row bench-terraces in Darjeeling

4. Tea-pluckers in Java

acreage by 45 per cent when the comparison between the recorded areas in 1941 and 1952 is made.[6, 9]

AFRICA

In Africa tea was being grown at the Durban Botanic Gardens in 1850 and developed into a local plantation industry of small extent in Natal after a coffee failure in 1877 similar to that in Ceylon.[6] In 1943 there were 2,000 acres but these have subsequently gone out of cultivation.

The oldest continuing tea industry in Africa is that of Malawi. From an introduction of tea seed in 1878 there were no survivors, but the Church of Scotland Mission procured seed via Kew and Edinburgh in 1886 and 1888 respectively, and from the progeny of the plants thus raised the first estate was planted in 1891. Proprietary planting has continued in Malawi for a longer time than elsewhere, but is gradually giving way to company ownership.[9, 10]

Specimen plants were being raised in the three East African territories at Limuru (Kenya), Entebbe (Uganda) and Amani (Tanganyika) at the turn of the century, but it was not until the decade 1920–1930 that commercial development began to take place. Between 1921 and 1925 three companies started work on the eastern and western escarpments of the Rift Valley in Kenya, which immediately established a lead in tea production that it has never lost. In 1924 a commercial estate was established near Tukuyu in the Southern Highlands province of Tanganyika and in 1931 in the Usambara Mountains. In Uganda the significant advance in tea cultivation was delayed until the early 'thirties.[11, 12]

OTHER REGIONS

Russia now counts as one of the chief areas where tea is grown. In 1913 an acreage of eighteen hundred is recorded and the latest estimates (1962) reach a figure of 162,800 acres in Russian Transcaucasia (Georgia) on the shores of the Black Sea. In the course of development mechanical aids to cultivation, notably mechanical plucking, have been used.

Precise and statistical information about the extent of tea culture in the traditional tea countries of China, Japan and Indo-China is not easily available since the general pattern in these countries is that of a peasant cultivation. Points of interest are that, despite the smallness of holdings in Japan, the production is highly organized, and that in Formosa tea growing on a considerable scale is as recent as the conclusion of the Sino-Japanese war of 1895.[6]

4   The Development of Tea Culture

In addition to the major tea-producing territories there are almost a score of others where tea is now grown or has been given a trial. Their wide dispersion is evident from the following catalogue of localities: Malaya,* Burma (Shan States)*, Thailand*, Vietnam* Mauritius,* Belgian Congo (Leopoldville)*, Rhodesia,* Portuguese East Africa,* Ethiopia,* St. Helena, Cameroons,* Brazil,* Peru,* Argentine,* Paraguay, Colombia, Bolivia, Mexico, Martinique, Iran,* Carolina, Australia* (including New Guinea), Turkey,* and Corsica. Their latitudes range from 40° N. to 33° S. Those which at present are vigorous enough to produce an export surplus, and for which statistics are available, are recorded in the last chapter.

REFERENCES

1. UKERS, W. H., All About Tea, Tea and Coffee Trade Journal Co., New York, 1935.
2. KINGDON WARD, H., Nature, 1950, 165, 297.
3. CARPENTER, P. H., The Wealth of India (article on Camellia sinensis), C.S.I.R.I., Delhi, 1950.
4. Society for the Diffusion of Useful Knowledge, Penny Magazine, 1840, 9, 70.
5. WATT, G., Dictionary of the Economic Products of India, 1889, 2, 79; 6, 429.
6. MORRISON, R. D., Memorandum Relating to the Tea Industry and Tea Trade of the World, International Tea Committee, London, 1943.
7. ANON., Tropical Agriculturist, 1881, 1, 221.
8. Census of Agriculture, 1952, Ceylon Government Press, Colombo, 1956.
9. DENHAM, G. C., World Crops, 1954, 6, 314.
10. HADLOW, G. S. J., Quarterly Journal of the Tea Association, Nyasaland, 1939, 4, 7.
11. GREENWAY, P. J., East African Agricultural Journal, 1945, 11, 56.
12. EDEN, T., World Crops, 1954, 6, 203.

* Localities where tea is at the present time known to be grown.

Chapter II

CLIMATE AND SOILS

Climate—Soil Types—Soil Properties—Soil Acidity—Plant Indicators—Soil Profiles.

CLIMATE

EXCEPT in very general terms it is difficult to specify the ideal or the average climate that tea requires especially in respect of rainfall. Various attempts have been made to estimate the water lost in transpiration by various crops, both short-term and perennial, as a guide to water requirements. The general conclusion is that individual crops or plants do not have unique transpiration coefficients; and that the particular meteorological conditions, together with soil conditions, largely determine the amount of transpiration that will take place. E. W. Russell quoting from Lee's compilation of many different estimates for a variety of crops, gives a range of 24 to 36 inches for perennial irrigated crops for which regular water service is available.[1] Gadd estimated that tea transpired, on the average, 36 inches per annum in the conditions prevalent at the Tea Research Institute of Ceylon.[2]

The type of rainfall distribution is an important factor in assessing rainfall requirements. The equatorial zone normally enjoys two rainy seasons coinciding with the apparent course of the sun across the intertropic zone. Regions to the north and south show only one such passage and are subject to prolonged dry seasons. Eden gives the following examples of rainfall distribution conforming to these types.[3]

RAINFALL PATTERNS IN EAST AFRICAN TEA DISTRICTS
(Excess + or deficit − based on monthly averages)

Locality	Latitude	Annual Rainfall in.	Distribution J. F. M. A. M. J. J. A. S. O. N. D.
Fort Portal	0·40°N.	60	− − − + + − − + + + + −
Tukuyu	9·15°S.	97	+ + + + − − − − − − − +

5

Configuration of the land adds further complications. Although Ceylon is subject to both the south-west and north-east monsoons the mountain massif produces an imposing rain shadow which deprives the eastern tea districts of the benefits of the rain accompanying the south-west monsoon. The same phenomenon is associated with the protection of the western ghats in South India.

Prevailing temperatures are an additional conditioning factor and here elevation is an important characteristic in modifying transpiration losses. The temperature range at a given elevation is also markedly influenced by whether or not the region in question enjoys a continental or an oceanic climate. On a rough comparison, the upland tea districts of Ceylon have a temperature range corresponding with situations in the Highlands of Kenya some 1,500 feet higher in altitude. In regions subject to protracted dry periods, overcast skies during dry weather and occult precipitation in the form of mist play a significant part in modifying drought conditions. Such occult precipitation can be influenced by the planting of wind belts and shade trees, and Hursh has emphasized this in relation to tea-planting areas in the Southern Highlands, Tanganyika.[4] Wind is a vital factor in promoting transpiration. During the first quarter of the year 1953, the Tea Research Institute of East Africa recorded windy days during the dry season at Kericho and showed that the evaporation from a free water surface was increased by amounts up to forty-five per cent in excess of that on windless days.[5]

In general there does not seem to be a decisive upper limit to the amount of rainfall under which tea will grow vigorously. In Ceylon there are districts receiving over two hundred inches where tea does well. On the other hand there is a consensus of opinion that at fifty inches per annum, rainfall is marginal unless other climatic conditions, such as those enumerated above, provide mitigating circumstances. Without exception the rainfall in the dry weather period is critical (because rainfall patterns are such that the rainy seasons provide more than enough), and a study of such records as are available shows that, if monthly averages fall below two inches over a period of several months, crop production suffers severely.

Although in certain areas of Georgia (U.S.S.R.) snow falls in the winter, there is no doubt that temperatures below freezing point are inimical to tea, particularly when followed, as is usual after night frost, by a rapid rise in daily temperatures toward the middle of the day, thus engendering scorch. Mann quotes average monthly temperatures for both tropical and semi-tropical areas which show that whilst the monthly maxima do not differ widely in the two areas and are mainly confined to the range 70°–84° F., the monthly minima

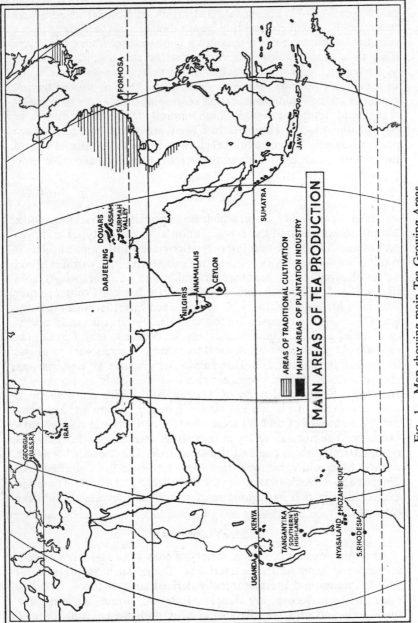

FIG. 1   Map showing main Tea Growing Areas

range from 22°–72° F.[6] In general, mean minimum temperatures below 55° F. are likely to bring about damage to the foliage and a cessation of growth; mean maximum temperatures above 85° F. are likely to be accompanied by humidities so low that a similar cessation of active development is inevitable. From these considerations it may be reasonably inferred that tea is suitable as a crop in regions having moderate to high rainfalls in excess of evaporation, and which maintain equable temperatures with high humidity throughout the greater part of the season. These, as has been previously mentioned, are predominatingly the equatorial regions at high or low altitudes, and the semi-tropical areas with summer rain to modify excessive temperatures.

SOIL TYPES

The range of soil types on which tea is grown is remarkably wide. Mann has summarized the existing knowledge of soil types and properties and his review and interpretations need little alteration as a result of subsequent work.[6] Some of the best tea in the world is found on the alluvium of the Brahmaputra valley and on soils formed from the wash of old sandstone on the north bank. Contemporary alluvium, for reasons that will be explained later, is unsuitable for tea. Other alluvial deposits are found in the Douars district in northeast India, and in Malawi. By way of contrast many good tea soils are old sedentary soils derived from archaic rocks such as gneiss in Darjeeling, Ceylon and Tanganyika, or granites in Uganda and certain areas in Japan. Volcanic rocks are the basis of tea soils in Indonesia, Kenya and parts of Tanganyika. There are also small areas of tea soils of a highly individual character. Japan and Formosa provide examples of diluvial soils, though these are not of high productivity. The Surmah valley in India has two radically different soil types intermingled in one and the same area. The "teelah" soils are derived from old sandstone and form low hummocks raised like pimples above black swamp soils, known locally as bheel. These are extraordinarily rich in organic matter and have a water table near the surface.

SOIL PROPERTIES

As may be expected, such a variety of soils shows widely different textural and structural characteristics. Some, such as the alluvial soils of Assam and the volcanically derived soils of the Rift Valley escarpments in Kenya, are devoid of stones. Some, including the bheel soils and grey clay flats of Assam, and the volcanic soils of Kenya, have little or no coarse sand fraction. These latter when suspended in water will pass freely through the pores of a Whatman filter paper. Loams predominate but there are sufficient sandy soils to falsify the assumption that light soils are necessarily unsuitable for tea. Mechanical analysis of tea soils gives little clue to their cultural suitability, particularly in Africa. Milne and Calton[7] in an East African survey heavily discounted the usefulness of such data because they found no consistent relationship between mechanical composition and field properties. The accompanying table of mechanical analyses shows the constitution of some of the very diverse soils from representative tea districts. They are determined by the old method due to Hall. The last four have not been corrected for loss on ignition which is not reported in the records. They merely serve to illustrate the dissimilarity of soils judged practically to be suitable for tea.

MECHANICAL ANALYSES OF TEA SOILS

Fraction		Soil							
	A.	B.	C.	D.	E.	F.	G.	H.	I.
Coarse Sand ..	16	—	—	32	21	20	34	24	2
Fine Sand	34	7	17	18	20	19	33	39	4
Silt	27	33	43	28	25	36	22	29	11
Clay	17	11	28	5	20	25	10	6	82
Loss on Ignition ..	6	33	8	16	15				

Key

A. Brahmaputra alluvium, Assam
B. Bheel soil, Surmah Valley
C. Clay flat, Surmah Valley
D. High Range, S. India
E. Nilgiris, S. India

F. Central Province, Ceylon
G. Uva Province, Ceylon
H. Pengalengan Plateau, Java
I. Kiambu, Kenya

Few satisfying conclusions can be drawn from the accumulated data of nutrient content of tea soils. In conjunction with the cropping records from manurial experiments, such data have cogency, but alone they give little guidance in assessing suitability for tea culture. In general, tea soils are of only moderate fertility owing to severe erosion and leaching. They are low in bases and phosphorus and their nitrogen content is very variable. It does not appear that any hard and fast distinction can be made, as regards nitrogen status, between forest and grassland soils in comparable localities, at any rate where tea has been established for some time. Vageler[8] and Eden[9] have stressed the point that the closed nutrient economy of undisturbed forest does not reflect a nutrient status as high as the rank growth of the vegetation might casually suggest. Moreover, when land is opened out of forest, the disturbance and destruction involved frequently lead to rapid wastage of fertile top soil. It is at least probable that the greater fertility of forest soils is associated with easier penetration of roots than with any intrinsic nutritional superiority. Figures for nitrogen content quoted by Bruce[10] for Ceylon forest soils are extremely variable and are not superior to those recorded by Eden[11] for the patana grassland of the montane regions. The whole question is complicated by subsequent cultural treatment. A series of analyses from virgin grassland and adjoining tea fields, of varying age up to fifty years, at the Tea Research Institute of Ceylon shows, according to Eden's classification, an actual increase in nitrogen content as cultivation periods increase. Doubtless the complex relationships between pruning leaf-fall, green and artificial manures systematically incorporated with the soil are responsible. Cooper[12] came to a similar conclusion from a series of formal experiments on the subject. He found that the increased production of pruning leaf due to manuring led to a progressive increase of soil nitrogen.

SOIL ACIDITY

Of the chemical characteristics of tea soils the one of dominant importance is that of soil reaction. Soil scientists agree that in normal circumstances there is an upper limit to the pH value of soils in which tea will thrive. This limit occurs between pH 6·0 and 6·5. At the other end of the range there appears to be no limiting value. Moderately good tea can be found growing at pH values of 4·5 and a few have been reported as low as 4·0, the lowest value attainable without the presence of free acid.

It is sometimes stated in the literature (Thomas[13] and Jacks[14]) that tea is a calcifuge and that the preference for acid conditions is associated with the generally low calcium status of leached acid soils. Whilst it is true that tea does not grow healthily on soils of high base saturation, and shows very distinctive pathological symptoms (which will be reviewed later) when attempts are made to do so, it cannot be rightly maintained that tea is a calcifuge. Normal tea leaf, as plucked, contains on the average more than 0·5 per cent of calcium, and, of the bases found in the leaf dry matter, calcium is the most abundant with the exception of potash. The calcium is present in the form of calcium oxalate (Child[15]). De Haan found that tea plants entirely deprived of calcium would not grow satisfactorily. There is thus a *prima facie* case for considering the question of high soil reaction not as a harmful characteristic *per se*, nor as a necessary condition for the existence of a calcifuge species, but as a symptom of some other disturbing factor.

Chenery[16] has pointed out that tea is an aluminium accumulator.

Certain species and genera, and one whole family of flowering plants, have been found to contain very high concentrations of aluminium in their tissues. Three hundred parts per million is a normal figure for most species: an arbitrary threshold of one thousand parts per million is set for accumulators. Tea contains up to 17,000 parts per million. The tropical soils on which tea is grown are rich in sesquioxides of iron and aluminium. At pH values around 6·5 the exchangeable aluminium is extractable only with difficulty in small quantities. At these reaction values tea shows the adverse symptoms generally associated with unsuitable pH values, and the aluminium content of the tissues is diminished. It may be that aluminium plays some regulating role in the nutrient economy of tea, perhaps in respect of toxic ions such as manganese. Or the unbalance revealed in the aluminium uptake may be an accentuated example of a type of unbalance that may develop in other ions when soils poorly supplied with bases are loaded with a preponderance of one or two of them. Kellogg and Davol[21] support this view and go to the extent of suggesting that lime or heavy fertilizer applications on latosols act in this manner.

Carpenter and Harler,[17] and later Harrison[18] noted the drop in pH values when soils suspended in neutral salt solutions were compared with those in water suspensions, and they further noted the washing out of aluminium in the neutral salt solutions. The titratable acidity of these solutions they termed "reserve" acidity and maintained that when two soils showed the same pH value, that which had the greater reserve acidity was the more suitable for tea. Taken in conjunction with Chenery's findings, this earlier work supports the view that the available aluminium status of the soil is a diagnostic characteristic of a good tea soil. Schofield[19] has explained the physico-chemical basis of this effect and has drawn the conclusion that the clay fractions of acid soils are aluminium clays and not hydrogen clays.

This emphasis on the part that aluminium plays in the relationship of tropical soils to tea culture has brought into use again the Comber test for soil acidity.[20] A saturated alcoholic solution of potassium thiocyanate agitated with markedly acid soils generates a blood-red colour due to the formation of ferric thiocyanate. In tropically weathered soils high iron and aluminium contents are closely associated, and when the colour reaction occurs, a high degree of aluminium availability can be assumed. The pH values at which only faint coloration takes place, or at which the solution remains colourless, correspond with those previously stated to be outside the workable range for tea culture. In East Africa, Child[15] has found Comber's test to be accurate enough for general survey work, and, in the hands of the planter, much simpler than colorimetric pH determinations with indicators. With soils of high clay content, the need to clear the suspensions of soil and indicator with barium sulphate, and the absorption of the dye from the solution, detract from ease of manipulation in the field. Comber's test works well so long as the soils are not damp enough to dilute the alcoholic concentration unduly.

PLANT INDICATORS

Although formal chemical and mechanical analyses are of value in choosing soils suitable for tea it is advisable to supplement the information they provide by a more general assessment of the soil characteristics of a proposed site. In this assessment, the type of vegetation naturally growing there is potentially informative, especially as regards the presence or absence of "indicator plants" associated with well-defined soil properties and crop requirements.

Mann[6] classifies albizzias as indicator plants, which is reasonable, considering that the remote habitats of prehistoric tea were albizzia forests. In Ceylon and South India bracken has long been regarded as an indicator, and may well serve in that capacity in Africa if attention is also paid to the rainfall pattern. In the montane regions of Africa bracken can flourish on a rainfall of no more than 40 inches which is not sufficient for economic crops of tea.

The most reliable plant indicators for tea are the aluminium accumulators previously mentioned which have been classified in detail by Chenery and used successfully by him and the present writer in Uganda and to a less extent in other East African localities.[22]

The most easily recognized of these plants are members of the genus *Dissotis* in the family *Melastomataceae*. They are easily recognized by their bright flowers and the characteristic venation of their leaves. Their prominent veins all diverge from the base of the leaf without a distinctive mid-rib, and converge again to the apex, producing a pattern rather like the lines of longitude on the surface of a terrestrial globe.

Common in Uganda are *D. brazzaei*, a lilac-flowered square-stemmed shrub; *D. violacea* with bright magenta flowers two inches in diameter; and *D. irvingiana* (synonym: *Osbeckia abyssinica*) with bright pink flowers. A near relation, *Osbeckia octandra*, is a common weed of tea land in Ceylon.

Other aluminium accumulators are those members of the family *Rubiaceae* that have bright blue fruits. One of these, *Craterispermum laurinum*, a small tree, was a decisive factor in the choice of a tract of land for tea cultivation in Uganda remote from other tea areas, a choice since amply justified by experience. Amongst the ferns the genus *Gleichenia* is found both in Uganda and in established tea areas in Ceylon.

SOIL PROFILES

The ecology of plants indicative of potentially good tea soils naturally includes the consideration of their root distribution. Consequently for this and well-known physical reasons a study of the soil profile is essential before allocating land for tea. Sampling tools are inadequate when prospecting for likely sites. Deep holes not less than three feet and preferably of five feet depth are needed. The tea plant has only feeble powers of root penetration through stiff and compacted soils. Pans, whether of gravel or clay, offer an almost impenetrable barrier to root growth. The root range of the plants in the original plant association is a valuable index of permeability when assessing the suitability of new sites. A good deal can also be inferred from soil colour. Whilst there are well-defined exceptions, such as well-drained bheel soils, red soils are usually superior to black or grey ones. If the subsoil is not red, or red-brown, indicating a high state of oxidation of iron compounds, a condition of impeded drainage can usually be inferred. Well-drained and permeable soils are essential for satisfactory growth of tea, and to have assurance on this point the subsoil must always be examined. The need for adequate drainage is well illustrated on the clay flat soils of parts of the Surmah valley. Here deep V-shaped open drains to a depth of about six feet are essential. For two or three rows on either margin, the growth of tea is distinctly more vigorous, with the consequence that the plucked surface of tea bushes on these fields presents the appearance of a series of moderate undulations, with peaks at the drains and hollows at the mid-points between them. Though the effect is to some extent accentuated by the spreading of the excavated earth from the drains, the prime cause is undoubtedly the superior aeration of the soil mass contiguous to the drains.

Mann places great emphasis on the need for high organic matter content of tea soils. In general this is a truism, but in particular it needs some amplification: appearance is not always a sound guide. Many highly coloured red loams have an organic matter content considerably in excess of what would be inferred from their appearance. Contrariwise some intensely black soils are not high in humus content. Furthermore, apart from the reservations previously made about soils of high humus content and impeded drainage, the potentialities of soils of high organic matter content are sometimes delusory. The bheel soils of the Surmah valley become denatured after prolonged cultivation. They dry out rapidly, become powdery and are difficult to wet. Eden[11] has recorded a similar state of affairs in the patana top soils of Ceylon. In Malawi the high organic matter of certain tea soils immobilizes available copper, and, in order to obtain satisfactory fermentation during manufacturing processes recourse has been had to spraying with copper compounds. This aspect will be dealt with in detail at a later stage.

To sum up, tea requires deep, permeable, well-drained acid soils of which the tropical red earths form the most extensively cultivated group in tea-producing countries.

REFERENCES

1. RUSSELL, E. J., and E. W., *Soil Conditions and Plant Growth*, 8th edn., London, 1950.
2. GADD, C. H., *Tea Quarterly*, 1935, **8**, 20.
3. EDEN, T., *World Crops*, 1954, **6**, 203.
4. *East African Agriculture and Forestry Research Organization Annual Report*, 1952.
5. Tea Research Institute of East Africa, *Proceedings of the First Conference*, 1953, Pamphlet No. 6.
6. MANN, H. H., *Tea Soils*, Technical Communication No. 32, Commonwealth Bureau of Soil Science, 1935.
7. MILNE, G. and CALTON, W. E., *East African Agricultural Journal*, 1943, **8**, 202.
8. VAGELER, P., *An Introduction to Tropical Soils*, Macmillan, London, 1933.
9. EDEN, T., *Elements of Tropical Soil Science*, Macmillan, London, 1947.
10. BRUCE, A., *Annals of the Royal Botanical Gardens, Peradeniya, Ceylon*, quoted by Mann.[6]
11. EDEN, T., *Journal of Soil Science*, 1951, **2**, 43.
12. COOPER, H. R., *Nitrogen Utilization in Tea*, Indian Tea Association, Memorandum No. 6, 1939.
13. THOMAS, A. S., *East African Agricultural Journal*, 1941, **7**, 24.
14. JACKS, G. V., *Tropical Soils in relation to Tropical Crops*, Technical Communication No. 34, Commonwealth Bureau of Soil Science.
15. CHILD, R., *The Selection of Soils suitable for Tea*, Tea Research Institute of East Africa, Pamphlet No. 5, 1953.
16. CHENERY, E. M., *Plant and Soil*, 1955, **6**, 174.
17. CARPENTER, P. H. and HARLER, C. R., *Quarterly Journal*, Indian Tea Association, 1921, 121.
18. HARRISON, C. J., ibid., 1930, 170.
19. SCHOFIELD, R. K., *Soils and Fertilizers*, 1946, **9**, 265.
20. COMBER, N. M., *Trans. Faraday Soc.*, 1924, **19**, 567.
21. KELLOG, C. E. and DAVOL, F. D., *Inst. Nat. pour l'Etude Agron. Congo Belg. Série Scient.* 46, 1949.
22. CHENERY, E. M., 1960. Private communication.

5. Tea country at foot of Mlanje Mountain, Nyasaland

6. Leaf transportation to factory, Sumatra

Chapter III

BOTANICAL CHARACTERISTICS

Taxonomy—General Botanical Characters—Periodic Shoot-Growth.

TAXONOMY

THE botanical name of the tea plant has had a chequered history, and only recently has uniformity in nomenclature been achieved by assigning to it the designation *Camellia sinensis* under which name tea is listed in the Index Kewensis.[1, 2] The confusion dates from the time of Linnaeus' original description. In the first volume of the *Species Plantarum* (May 1753) tea is described as *Thea sinensis*: in the second edition Linnaeus abandoned the name *Thea sinensis* and described two specimens, one with six petals and one with nine, as *Thea bohea* and *Thea viridis* respectively. It has now been agreed that the separation of *Thea* and *Camellia* as distinct genera is spurious, and as, according to the International Rules of Nomenclature (Article 46), in the fusion of two allied groups the name of the earlier should be maintained, the name *Camellia sinensis* has prevailed. For many years the dual nomenclature was reflected in the name *Camellia thea* which was used, by agreement, by botanists in India and Ceylon (Wight and Barua;[3] Bond[4]); Cohen Stuart in Indonesia used the name *Camellia theifera*. Now that uniformity has been reached, Sealy[5] gives the complete designation as *Camellia sinensis* (L) O. Kuntze. There has also been some variation in the name of the family to which the genus *Camellia* is assigned: Theaceae and Ternstroemiaceae are synonymously used with a growing preference for the former.

The question of varieties is a difficult one. The closest approach to varietal distinctions is found in the use of the term "jat." Usually the word has no more than a geographical significance, indicating the district or plantation from which the seed has been derived, but it is also used to separate, on the basis of foliar characteristics, what appear to be distinct types. Thus the so-called indigenous Assam jats are described as "light-leaved," thus contrasting their colour with "dark-leaved" jats. Some plants have leaves that are comparatively narrow in relation to their breadth; are profusely indented at the margin, and have flat rather dull-coloured laminae. These

15

types are called low-jat and are frequently referred to as china or hybrid-china jats. Others have larger leaves, wider in proportion, with blunter tips and fewer serrations, and a crinkled (bullate) surface: these are high-jat plants.

From these foliar and other characteristics, attempts have been made to describe distinguishable varieties. Sealy,[5] in his re-examination of the genus *Camellia*, after collating all known specimens and descriptions concludes that most of the postulated varieties have no taxonomic status other than as synonyms of two undoubted varieties which he names *Camellia sinensis* var. *sinensis*, embracing the "China" types, and *C. sinensis* var. *assamica*, the Assam types. The plethora of variants, e.g. *viridis, bohea, stricta, cambodiensis*, used by Watt, Cohen Stuart[6] and Carpenter,[7] is thus thinned out root and branch. Sealy allows a few instances of sub-varietal distinction, e.g. *C. sinensis* var. *sinensis* f. *parviflora* (Miq) Sealy and *C. sinensis* var. *sinensis* f. *macrophylla* Sieb. These are described as "fixed variants".

Within a variety there are noticeable differences in appearance between individual bushes or populations of bushes. Wight[8] classified these into named "agrotypes" with reference to certain metrical measurements, the most informative of which he finds to be the average frequency of calcium oxalate crystals in specialized cells of the vascular tissues (phloem parenchyma).

GENERAL BOTANICAL CHARACTERS

In natural conditions, tea grows into a small tree about thirty feet high. It has a rather straggling habit, but when grown in isolation or at wide planting distances, the better type bushes are roughly cone-shaped. It is tap-root dominant and puts out strong lateral roots. The root distribution pattern is distinctly variable and Tubbs[9] showed that to a considerable degree the variation was a clonal characteristic. Whilst some bushes develop deep laterals, others persist in putting out almost horizontal roots which never penetrate to any great depth. The extension roots give rise to prolific feeding roots, which when fully developed, are devoid of root hairs. Within a short distance of the root-cap these feeding roots become suberized. Butler,[10] Park,[11] Tunstall[12] and Webster[13] have found an endotrophic mycorrhiza in the feeding roots: its biological significance has not yet been determined. In plantation conditions the feeding roots are confined to a relatively shallow layer irrespective of whether or not cultivation is carried out. Eden,[14] by determining weights of roots at successive three-inch depths from a large number of samples under varying cultural treatments, found that at the twenty-four inch depth, the weight of feeding roots did not exceed five per cent of the weight

7. Contour planting, Tea Research Institute, Ceylon

8. Contour hedges, Kenya

9. Tea flowers

10. Tea fruit

for the total range. Apart from the recognized function of absorbing and conducting water and nutrients, the roots, when they reach a diameter of between one and two millimetres, lay down starch granules in their cells, thus becoming important storage organs. This stored carbohydrate has a critical function after pruning operations and further consideration will be given to this aspect of the physiology of the bush in the chapter on pruning.

The development of the aerial portion of the plant proceeds from the main axis of the seedling, or cutting, which puts out leaves whose phyllotaxy is alternate. New leaves and branches develop from buds in the axils of mature leaves. These leaves are evergreen, obovate-lanceolate in shape, and acuminate. Normal mature leaves are serrated at the margin. As previously indicated, their size differs according to jat. Those produced in the early stages of growth, and after pruning, are larger than those subsequently formed. Leaves ranging in size from one to ten inches can be found in fields of mixed race and age. Leaves are generally glabrous with some sparsely distributed hairs on the under surface. The buds and internodes are more profusely hairy. Old leaves are leathery in texture, highly polished on the upper surface and deep green in colour.

A transverse section of the leaf discloses a heavily cuticularized epidermis, which gives the characteristic glossy shine, and one or two layers of rectangular pallisade cells according as the leaves have developed as shade or sun leaves. Beneath this regular array is the spongy mesophyll of squat irregular-shaped cells and the lower epidermis. The stomata with prominent guard cells are on the lower surface. Embedded in the mesophyll are occasional cells, sclereids, exhibiting marked lignification. These sclereids are typical and they are easily recognized in manufactured leaf. They are of use in diagnosing the presence or absence of adulteration of made tea by other leafy material. Fatty bodies and inorganic salt crystals can be distinguished under a low power magnification amongst the cell contents. The constituents of the cells will be described in the chapter describing the chemistry of the tea leaf.

The globular flower-buds are borne in the axils of scale-leaves, variously described as perules by Sealy[5] and cataphylls by Bond,[4] and develop either singly or in clusters. In camellias the flowers have pedicels that may be either long or short: *Camellia sinensis* has a short pedicel. The fully developed flower has a persistent calyx with a variable number of sepals usually 5 to 7. The petals, corresponding in number to the sepals, are white with a smooth waxy appearance. At the base they are fused to one another and to the numerous stamens (20 to 200 in typical Camellia species). In shape the petals are obovate, emarginate and internally concave. The stamens are long with yellow twin-celled anthers and are free above two or three millimetres (Fig. 2). The ovary is hairy and has a single style split into 3 to 5 arms. The green fruit is three-celled and thick-walled, shiny at first but duller and slightly rough later. According to Sealy this thick wall is characteristic of the Camellia species that have short pedicels naked at anthesis. The fruit dehisces by splitting from the apex into three

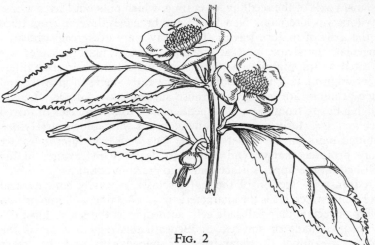

FIG. 2
Tea: leaves and flowers

valves. The brown seed is typically thin-shelled, about half an inch in diameter, semi-globose in shape or rounded at the back and wedge-shaped in front. It contains two large cotyledons which when separated clearly show the embryonic radicle and plumule. The cotyledons are notable for their high oil content (up to 20 per cent by weight).[15] Child[16] has shown that the fatty acid ester components of this oil are similar to those of olive oil for which it is a recognized culinary substitute. This oil absorbs certain fumigants, notably methyl bromide, used to eradicate lepidopterous borers and their use may lead to the death of the seed.

PERIODIC SHOOT-GROWTH

One of the most interesting characteristics of tea shoots is the distinct periodicity of growth that is basically unconnected with climate or other environmental conditions. These rhythms are well known to tea planters for their maxima are the recognized "flushing" periods and their minima the dormant "banjhi" periods: they have therefore practical as well as physiological significance (Fig. 3). Bond[4, 17] has examined the phenomenon in great detail. In outline the picture he gives of the typical sequence of development is as follows:

At the period of dormancy the terminal leaf of the shoot has attained full size and discloses a young "banjhi" bud which is about

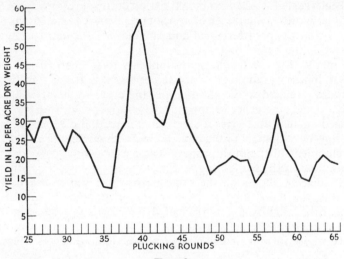

FIG. 3

Periodicity of Tea 'Flushes'. (The plucking rounds are at nine-day intervals and extend over the second year of the pruning cycle. Ceylon data)

5 mm. long and is neither so long nor so fat as a normal active "flush" bud, i.e. a bud that will develop into a pluckable shoot. The bud swells but shows no sign of breaking for a considerable time. Then the outermost appendage breaks free and produces, not a normal leaf but a mere scale-leaf (cataphyll). This is followed by the unfolding of a second appendage similar to the first: the first scale-leaf commonly drops off. At the breaking of the second scale leaf the tip of a new leaf becomes visible within; and, as this develops, it is seen to be larger than a scale-leaf but neither in size nor shape similar to a normal flush-leaf. It is small, blunt, and has not the usual closely serrated margin. This is the so-called fish-leaf or in Indian terminology the "janam." Its position on the shoot is of the very greatest importance when considering standards of plucking. As the

bud continues to unfold, normal leaves are produced which grow in size to that of mature flush-leaves with elongating internodes. After the development of a number of normal leaves the shoot again goes banjhi, thereby ending one complete period, which is followed by further ones of the same type. This periodicity is independent of plucking, and during a single phase the typical growth consists of two scale-leaves, a fish-leaf and four flush-leaves. At the time when a banjhi bud begins to break all the initials of the appendages that will emerge, before the next banjhi period occurs, are already formed: in other words the number of appendages between one banjhi pause and the next is predetermined and unalterable, and can be found by dissecting the banjhi bud.

Superficially, the banjhi period appears to the agriculturist to be one of inactivity: in fact it is not so because it is at this time that the primordia related to the ensuing flushing cycle are being laid down. The ordered emergence of appendages—scale- or flush-leaves—when plotted against time gives a series of exponential curves illustrating the slow development of the bud and scale-leaves, and the more rapid development of the flush proper. These exponential curves are discontinuous at the banjhi stages. Since the physiological condition of even adjacent shoots on the same bush will never be exactly comparable, the representation of average performance in the flushing cycle, calculated from a number of shoots, leads to a blurring of the discontinuity of the growth periods. This gives rise to a continuous curve whose form is that of a sequence of sigmoid curves which can be fitted with logistic equations of the type $y = \dfrac{K}{1 + C\,e^{at}}$ where t is time and K, C and a are constants. In Bond's view the determinant of whether a scale-leaf, fish-leaf or a normal flush-leaf will be produced depends upon growth rate as affected by the supply of nutrients in general, and of nitrogen in particular. In the event of positive nitrogen deficiency a shoot, instead of growing a normal quota of two scale-leaves and a fish-leaf before producing normal flush, will throw out an extended series of undeveloped appendages. Contrariwise, under specially abundant conditions of nutrition a continuous series of flush-leaves may emerge such as are seen in the leading shoots that appear from time to time on vigorous bushes.

The general pattern of rhythmic growth is modified in detail by extraneous factors. That of nutrition has been touched upon: in addition climate is of obvious importance as is also the artificial procedure of plucking. It is impossible to regulate plucking according to the niceties of this elegant demonstration of periodicity, but when its nature is understood an empirical solution of the problem is possible. The frequency of plucking operations must dovetail into the rhythm of this periodicity so that banjhi periods will not upset the regular plucking rounds : and, equally, so that the rapid growth periods of flush are not truncated, thus throwing the shoots back into the slow development phase of immature scales and fish-leaves.

REFERENCES

1. Index Kewensis, Supplement, 1886–95.
2. UKERS, W. H., *All About Tea*, Tea and Coffee Trade Journal Co., New York, 1935.
3. WIGHT, W. and BARUA, D. N., *The Tea Plant in Industry*, Indian Tea Association, Calcutta, Memorandum No. 7, 1939.
4. BOND, T. E. T., *Annals of Botany*, 1942, **6**, 607.
5. SEALY, J. B., *A Revision of the Genus Camellia*, Royal Horticultural Society, 1958.
6. COHEN STUART, C. P., *Voorbereidende onderzockingen ten dienst van de Selektie der Thee plant, Mededeelingen v.h. Proefstation voor Thee*, XL, 1916.
7. CARPENTER, P. H., *The Wealth of India*, Article on *Camellia sinensis*, C.S.I.R.I., Delhi, 1950.
8. WIGHT, W., *Proceedings of Ninth Conference*, Indian Tea Association, Calcutta, 1951.
9. TUBBS, F. R., *Tea Quarterly*, 1946–7, **18**, 82.
10. BUTLER, F. J., *Report on some Diseases of Tea and Tobacco in Nyasaland*, Dept. of Agriculture, Zomba, 1928.
11. PARK, M., *Tropical Agriculturist*, 1928, **70**, 171.
12. TUNSTALL, A. C., *Notes on Root Diseases of Tea in N.E. India*, Indian Tea Association, Memorandum No. 8, 1940.
13. WEBSTER, B. N., *Tea Quarterly*, 1953, **24**, 26.
14. EDEN, T., *Emp. J. exp. Agric.*, 1940, **8**, 269.
15. VERHAAR, G. and DEYS, W. B., *Arch. v.d. Thee Cultuur*, 1948, **16**, 37.
16. CHILD, R., *Tropical Agriculturist*, 1935, **84**, 71.
17. BOND, T. E. T., *Annals of Botany*, 1945, **9**, 1183.

Chapter IV

PLANTING MATERIAL

*Tea Seed Bearers—Viability of Tea Seed—Grading of Seed
—Nursery Technique—Transference of Nursery Plants to the
Field—Vegetative Propagation and Selection.*

THE traditional source of planting material is seed, which is convenient to use but produces very variable plants; witness any field of commercial tea raised in this way. Since a generation from seed to seed may occupy from four to fifteen years, plant breeding with tea is obviously a long-term project. There are, as yet, no pure line varieties produced *ad hoc* by breeding techniques on a commercial scale.

Wight[9] at the Tocklai Experimental Station has started a scheme of progressive improvement of seed-bearer plantations (seed baries). By planting in nurseries the seed from better-than-average trees, it is possible at an early stage to compare the desirable characteristics of the progeny of these trees with those from seed representative of the whole bari. From this more rigorous selection, clones are raised to plant as a new bari, which in due course gives an improved generation of seed. By continued alternation of selection by seedling performance, on the one hand, with the establishment of clonal seed baries on the other, continual progress in the production of commercial seed of superior quality is made practicable. Further improvement is possible if in an eventual two-clone bari one of the clones is a "combiner", i.e. one whose pollen imposes dominant characteristics on the progeny, thus enhancing uniformity.

At present the most expeditious way of improving planting material is the large-scale multiplication and proving of vegetatively propagated clones from selected mother-bushes in commercial fields. In this chapter both methods of raising planting material will be described, namely from seed and from vegetative cuttings.

TEA SEED BEARERS

It is customary to establish limited and separate areas of tea to make provision for seed requirements, though occasionally seed is picked

22

from bearing bushes. In general only the poorer strains will flower and seed freely on the plucked bushes, and seed gathered in this manner is not of a desirable quality. In Assam, where the cultivation of tea seed bearers has received much attention, the areas are specially planted for the purpose and the young plants are carefully selected for vigorous growth, uniformity and, as far as possible, bearing in mind the constancy of one illegitimate parent, for prolific bearing capacity. In many instances, however, tea seed bearers start their life as ordinary plants in a commercial field originally planted for cropping purposes. The procedure followed is to earmark bushes at regular intervals which are allowed to grow freely until eventually the balance between the vegetative and reproduction phases changes and seed in sufficient quantities is produced. These seed bearers may remain as such in ordinary fields or, more commonly, the interspersed bearing bushes are removed. In practice either of these methods is easy of accomplishment but unsatisfactory in the long run. In the first place the method results in bearers of very heterogeneous type, some positively undesirable, and others relatively unproductive; and secondly in this system of conversion, insufficient spacing is an almost ubiquitous fault.

For adequate growth a stand of not more than a hundred trees per acre is essential, and for the best conditions not more than seventy is desirable. If the trees are too crowded their branches lose their lower foliage and they become misshapen. For both these reasons they carry fewer flower buds and they produce no new growth at the lower levels to act as replacement of those branches which, for various reasons, are broken or die back.

A young tea seed bearer ten to twelve feet high needs shaping by reducing the branches to a convenient number, such as six, which can be spaced so as to allow regular development of the crown. This is important not only to ensure adequate light but also to provide easy access by pollinating insects. The healthy preservation of the branches is an obvious necessity and trimming of branches should be carried out with considerable care. Clean cuts and protection of the cut surface with a bituminous paint, or other cover of a waterproof and fungicidal nature, should be a regular and normal practice; otherwise in the older tree loss of branches from wood-rot and die-back may severely limit productive capacity.

In many instances little attention to seed bearers is given after the tree has been established, it apparently being thought that as the bearers would grow in a milieu similar to forest, no cultivation would be necessary. On the contrary, seed bearers respond well to the application of fertilizers and the recommendations of the Tocklai

Experimental Station[1] have been found to be acceptable over a large range of conditions. These recommendations for a mature bearer are:

Sulphate of Ammonia	..	3 lb.
Superphosphate (18%)	..	1 lb.
Muriate of Potash	..	1 lb.

Soil cultivation in the physical sense is unnecessary except to control weed growth, to apply fertilizers and to provide a clean surface from which to collect the fallen seed. When the capsule is ripe it dehisces and the mature seed falls to the ground. Since tea seed quickly loses its viability, it should be collected as promptly as possible. During the height of the season daily collections are advisable.

VIABILITY OF TEA SEED

For the best results, tea seed should be used within a few days of picking, but this is not always possible particularly if it has to be transported over long distances. Although there are many tea estates that produce tea seed for sale, and they have empirically worked out suitable methods of storage, there is a lack of precise information on the subject. Leach[2] experimented successfully with storage in pits and succeeded in maintaining a reasonably high germination rate in seed a year old. Such protracted periods are not normally needed but occasionally there may be a carry-over from a bumper season that it is desired should not be lost. For the transport of seed over long distances the standard method is to pack in boxes in a matrix of damp powdered charcoal, separating the seeds layer by layer by means of brown paper. None of the various instructions found in planting manuals defines the moisture content that will preserve the seed from drying out on the one hand, or rotting on the other. Unpublished trials at the Tea Research Institute of East Africa show that a moisture content of approximately 15 per cent will preserve seed without either gain or loss of weight in the seed.

Storing or transporting seed in bulk without any precautions whatever leads to sweating and heating of the seed, with resultant loss in germination capacity. The use of a 50 : 50 decoction of fish glue and water, or of a plastic emulsion such as "Ceremul," is worth a trial. These preparations have been found useful in preservation of forest tree seeds. A diminution of up to 25 per cent in germination capacity may easily occur in tea seed unprotected for a period of ten days or a fortnight.

Owing to the prevalence of blister blight most tea-producing countries maintain an embargo on the importation of tea seed from districts affected by the disease. Opinions vary as to whether the risk is significant, but as it is an undeterminable one, other countries prefer not to run it.

Apart from possible blister blight infection there are risks of importing undesirable insect pests, particularly lepidopterous borers, when tea seed is moved from one locality to another. There are therefore various quarantine regulations and procedures at ports and stations of entry. These vary from country to country and in detail have no place in this book. As, however, tea seed has unusual delicacy, the use of fumigants without prior investigation of their specific effect on tea can be dangerous. In East Africa the popular and effective methyl bromide fumigant has been found to be quite unsuitable for tea seed, probably because of the high content of oil in which methyl bromide is soluble. The details of its effect still remain to be clarified because, though it can cause a hundred per cent loss of viability when seed is fumigated and remains unsown for forty-eight hours, the effect is relatively insignificant if seeds are placed in the germination beds immediately after the dispersion of the fumigant. Hot-water treatment (52° C. for 30 minutes) is a reliable destructant of borer larvae and has the advantage of enhancing germination. Leach's trials established the fact that a few hours' sun-drying of the seed, immediately before planting, had a similar good effect on germination. To what extent the effect is due to temperature or to the cracking of the seed is a matter of conjecture.

GRADING OF SEED

Two simple and complementary operations are commonly used to grade seed: sieving and immersion in water. Seed retained on a half-inch mesh is usually considered to have sufficient food reserves in the cotyledons to promote good embryonic growth. Some seeds will be empty and not a few may, by arrested development, have a considerable air space between the shell and the cotyledons. When this is so the apparent specific gravity of the seed will be low and the seed will float: normal seed will sink. Floaters are not necessarily bad seed, though Harler and Laycock's experiments in Malawi reflect the poorer germination and subsequent vigour of the floater fraction. If used for planting, floaters are best kept in separate beds. Though the water immersion is a very simple criterion it demands some care in operation. About five times the volume of water as of seed should be used and stirring should be carried out at intervals to rid seed surfaces of buoyant air bubbles. Half an hour's immersion is a maximum, otherwise saturation of the seed coat or cracks in its surface may lead to an apparently high and misleading percentage of sinkers. For the sinker fraction a germination percentage of less than 70 per cent is definitely unsatisfactory. Tea seed is a slow germinator and consequently germination tests are always in the nature of post-mortem examinations. Viable ungerminated seeds have been found after a year in germination beds. The Tea Research Institute of East Africa has experimented with triphenyl tetrazolium bromide (Grodex) as a rapid method of assessment. Whilst the consonance with germination trials is not absolute, the staining of the embryo, due to a red dye developed by the interaction of the test solution with the enzyme in the embryo, is a useful indication of the soundness of seed.

NURSERY TECHNIQUE

The direct planting of seed in the field (seed-at-stake) has in the past been practised on a considerable scale and is still occasionally encountered, but except in circumstances ideal in respect of both climate and soil it is unsatisfactory. Unless the plant makes good growth and gets its root system firmly established in the first growing season and is carefully preserved from undue competition of weeds, very heterogeneous stands of tea are likely to ensue. In modern practice, the preliminary rearing of plants in nurseries is the general rule.[3] The type and management of tea nurseries depend on local conditions. One characteristic is common to all methods, that meticulous care in nursery preparation, organization and maintenance has a far-reaching effect on the subsequent history of the plants when they are planted in the field and can no longer receive horticultural care.

The use of germinated seed in nurseries is by no means as common as, with advantage, it might be. Without this precaution irregularity of growth is inevitable because of the slow germination rate, previously mentioned, and of the competition which faster growing plants offer to the laggards. The variability in germination rate is shown by the following average percentages of germination during a three-month period in sixteen trials.

	1 month	2 months	3 months
Germination percentage ..	22	60	67

Heaps or beds of sand are the best media for germination. Trays covered with damp hessian are easy to handle when sorting out the germinated individuals, but they are difficult to maintain at a uniform temperature. Seeds set for germination should not touch each other and should be protected from sun and wind. Some heat will be generated by the germination process and this is advantageous in moderation. Twice a week the seeds need picking over, and as soon as the radicle is ready to emerge from the shell they should be planted.

Before preparing a nursery of great potential value a soil test for suitability of reaction is advisable. The prepared seed is commonly dealt with in one of two ways. It is either planted in a small container holding two to three pounds of prepared soil, or in a carefully cultivated bed. For raising seedlings in containers a variety of materials has been used. Baskets of split and plaited bamboo or folded banana leaves were the commonest, the choice being determined by local availability. Segments of giant bamboo have not generally been successful. These traditional materials have now been superseded by the plastic polythene sleeves. The 7-inch lay flat film tube of 150-gauge, cut to a length of twelve inches, makes a serviceable "pot", 4½-inch diameter, which, if carefully filled with soil, is not too constricted for adequate drainage. Wider tubes of heavier gauge greatly increase the cost. Where the coherence of the soil is such that loss may occur when the filled pots are moved, a single staple joining the bottom edge is useful. Seedlings can be grown in these containers until the tap root reaches the bottom and then be transferred to the planting hole without disturbance, after slitting the sleeve vertically and removing.

To say that nursery beds should be well and deeply cultivated and thoroughly drained is to state a truism, but in the light of experience it is necessary to do so. Twenty-four inches is the minimum depth permissible in order to promote a strong unforked tap-root. Any excavation into raw subsoil within this depth is sufficient indication that the nursery site is ill chosen. If the soil horizon is not reasonably uniform care is needed in cultivation, whether by hand or machine, to prevent inversion of the top and subsoil layers. For convenience in maintenance, beds should not exceed four feet in width, with easily accessible intervening paths and alley-ways. Whether beds shall be flat or raised and their sides revetted is a matter to be decided by the type of soil in which they are laid out.

At some time during the nursery period beds will need shading. Outside the equatorial latitudes, as for example in Assam, winter planting of nurseries can be started without shade but with a light vegetable mulch to prevent drying out of the beds. In most regions a frame shade some five feet from the ground constructed out of bamboo, fern, or grass is necessary, and it is well to erect it before planting operations begin. There has been some prejudice against repeated use of nursery sites, particularly where land and water access is easy. The consequent shifting of nursery sites to new ground has led to the erection of very impermanent structures often of doubtful efficiency. With suitable green manuring and fallowing after raising two nursery crops, satisfactory productivity of nurseries can be maintained. Their deterioration is less a matter of soil exhaustion than of retrogression in physical condition caused by continual, and frequently excessive, watering. Shade frames of a reasonably permanent type made with stout posts and interlacing wire or bamboo are in the long run the best proposition.

Live shade provided by growing leguminous bush plants, carefully controlled to give an umbrella shade, is frequently used, particularly in Assam where *Tephrosia candida* is suitably employed in this way. In other places its success is on the whole doubtful. Its canopy is never perfect; its drain on soil moisture can be very damaging; and in soils infested with eelworm of the genus *Meloidogyne* it has been found to increase the eelworm population to an extent which endangers the developing tea plants.

The spacing of seed in nursery beds has a marked effect on the growth and vigour of the young plant, which will continue to be evident when the plant is transferred to the field. As a general recommendation 6 inches by 6 inches square or triangular are the most suitable spacings, particularly if the plants are to be lifted whole and transplanted with roots and soil intact.

In the maintenance of nursery plants two points are of prime importance: water supply and shade regulation. As regards the former, excellent results are obtained by irrigation either of the overhead spray or channel type, if carefully controlled. The most prevalent fault in irrigation is excess which leads to malformation or death, totally or in part, of the tap-root. It is always better to give nurseries a thorough drenching at intervals of a few days, allowing the soil to come into equilibrium at field capacity for a considerable depth, than to risk creating a shallow semi-waterlogged layer on the surface at frequent intervals. Any sign of mosses and lichens on the nursery bed is an indication that such an undesirable moisture content is being maintained. This is particularly apt to occur under heavy shade.

As the nursery plants establish themselves shade can be usefully reduced and finally removed when the shade screen interferes with growth. This process must be gradual to allow leaves of shade habit to adjust themselves to more intense sunlight; otherwise scorch and defoliation will occur. A close nursery stand of robust plants has so large a transpiratory surface that during dry periods permanent wilting may supervene unless elaborate irrigation of the types mentioned is possible. Reduction of foliage by cutting back the plants immediately a temporary wilt is noticed will usually rectify conditions. Quite a light skiffing is generally sufficient, and it is desirable that no hard cutting back should be done. The reason for this is that these anti-drought precautions are usually necessary only in the latter stages of nursery growth, no great time before planting out. With the arrival of the rainy season severely pruned plants will rapidly renew their foliage at the expense of their stored reserves. If, as will be described in detail later, the plants are destined to be put into the field as cut-back stumps, this depletion of reserves may have a detrimental effect on subsequent growth, or even on survival.

TRANSFERENCE OF NURSERY PLANTS TO THE FIELD

The stage and form in which plants are ready to be transferred to the field depends on climatic and soil conditions and also on the type of growth stimulated by the nursery technique. Tea is tap-root dominant and ordinarily an uprooted nursery plant has a single vertical axis consisting of the main stem, with such lateral branches as the constricted space has allowed to grow, and a robust tap-root with only the rudiments of lateral roots. Such a plant can be success-fully planted whole if the soil is maintained round the roots. The use of some kind of transplanting instrument makes this possible and, in Assam, where the texture of the soil is ideal, the plant can be removed, with its natural clod of soil firmly attached, merely by care-fully digging round the plant with a special spade. This "bheti" planting is probably the best method of transplanting to be found, but in all its ease and perfection it is only applicable to Assam con-ditions. Elsewhere if "ball" planting is carried out the soil has to be compacted round the roots to prevent loss during transport. This is much less satisfactory because the soil becomes puddled, and the roots suffer deformation. All forms of transplanting with adherent soil involve the carrying of vast masses of soil from nursery to field site and the depletion of the nursery top soil to a corresponding extent. This technique is therefore only suitable where planting pro-grammes are small or where there is plenty of land available and no need to continue from year to year the use of the same site. The planting of young seedlings in the field with bare roots is consistently so disastrous as to need no consideration here.

In default of transplanting with roots and soil intact the method of stump or carrot planting is widely used. The underlying principle of this method is based on the fact that the roots of tea, and predomina-tingly the tap-root, is the main storage organ of the plant. For stump planting, seedlings are allowed to grow for a much longer period (up to three years) than is the case with other transplants. The stem of the plant is cut back to within a few inches of ground level and the resulting "carrot" is used as the precursor of a new developing plant. The system has many advantages. The bulk of material to be moved is small, and the risks of damage to the plants is limited. The stored food reserves in the tap-root are, in a good specimen, considerable, and can nourish new growth through dry periods which would severely weaken or kill a whole seedling subject to continual loss of foliage. All things considered, and excepting the special features of Assam planting, stumps are the most satisfactory planting material in circumstances where soil or climatic conditions are likely to be rigorous in the early stages of establishment.

The stage at which stumps can best be used is a matter of much debate. There must always be some latitude owing to practical difficulties caused by variation in planting and seed maturing seasons, but, in normal practice, a well-formed plant that at the stumping level of four inches has a stem diameter between $\frac{3}{8}$ in. and $\frac{1}{2}$ in. is vigorous enough to remove to the field. The advantages that are claimed for larger stumps are often counterbalanced by disadvantages that are not always realized. Whilst the larger the plant, the greater the expectation of adequate food reserves in the tap-root, there is no point in producing a root which will have to be severely truncated at the time of digging out to accommodate it in the planting hole. An extra year's growth in the nursery has in any event to be balanced against the loss of time in the field. The older the wood on which a stumping cut is made, the less viable the buds: the larger the cut the less chance there is that the wound will be totally occluded by new growth, and the greater the risk of perpetuating a wound that will be a focus for invasion by wood-rotting fungi at a point where the resultant damage is most dangerous. Excessively large nursery plants create difficulties in maintenance, particularly as has been previously remarked, in adequate watering. If they have to be cut back in order to diminish their size and transpirational surface and in subsequent growth draw upon reserves, it takes a considerable time before these reserves are again built up. By way of illustration of the set-back such treatment involves, an experiment on nursery plants from vegetatively propagated cuttings at the Tea Research Institute of East Africa may be quoted. Plants which were stumped only at the time of planting suffered less than 1 per cent casualties in the ensuing nine months. Plants a year older which were stumped at the same time, but which had also been cut back a year previously, had over 15 per cent failures: the extra year's growth under the defined circumstances was of no advantage.[4]

VEGETATIVE PROPAGATION AND SELECTION

The success of vegetative propagation as a means of producing planting material for commercial use depends upon the selection of plants that are above average in performance as regards both vigour of growth and manufacturable quality of the leaf, on the one hand; and upon a technique of propagation which is capable of being organized on a large scale on the other. The possibilities of selecting from commercial fields outstanding plants to serve as mother bushes for subsequent multiplication are immense, because experience shows that the greater part of the yield of an individual field is contributed by a relatively small number of bushes. Kehl[5] has published data of flush counts on a thousand individual bushes, randomly selected, in which the number of pluckable shoots collected during five consecutive plucking rounds ranged from twenty to more than three hundred. In a further trial, comprising 1,515 bushes, the extremes ranged from less than twenty to a thousand. The distribution of these individual bush yields was negatively skew to a very marked degree and less than 5 per cent of the bushes gave counts above the mean category value.

Eden[6] showed that, for purposes of selection, relatively few plucking rounds need be used to establish a criterion, whilst latterly Kehl is of the opinion that, in the first instance, selection by eye at the end of a pruning cycle is sufficient without the refinement of making flush counts or quantitative yield estimates. In practice the procedure is one of rejection, rather than selection, based on discarding bushes that exhibit the following unsatisfactory characteristics:

(1) Lax plucking tables.
(2) Upright habit as opposed to spreading habit.
(3) Scarcity of foliage leaves below plucking table.
(4) Tendency to flowering.
(5) Prevalence of dormant buds (banjhi).
(6) Close internodes.

From the remainder a further discard is needed of those bushes which are in abnormally favourable positions such as adjoining vacancies, roads or paths or which are growing in spoil earth.

In this manner potentially high-yielding bushes are reserved for further consideration as regards susceptibility to disease, especially blister blight, and manufacturable quality. The former must obviously be carried out during the peak of a blister blight attack. As regards the latter, at this stage no more delicate procedure than mincing the leaf and observing its rate of fermentation is needed. Certain strains of tea are notably poor fermenters and this appears to be associated with a definite genetical factor.

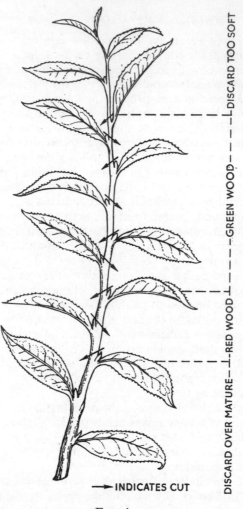

DISCARD TOO SOFT

GREEN WOOD

RED WOOD

DISCARD OVER MATURE

→ INDICATES CUT

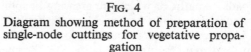

Fig. 4

Diagram showing method of preparation of single-node cuttings for vegetative propagation

The technique of propagation by cuttings has received close attention from the various research institutes. Visser[10] in Ceylon and Green[14] in Kenya have given detailed accounts of experimental work which not only confirms but also extends the earlier work in

11. Tea seed-bearers

12. Vegetative propagation Nursery (Assam)

13. Spray irrigation on shaded nursery, Kenya

14. Single node cuttings in propagation bed, Tanganyika

Ceylon,[7] India[8] and East Africa.[4] It is, however, evident that their recommendations are in part influenced by local circumstances which may not apply elsewhere.

There is agreement in all quarters that single-node whole-leaf cuttings are the best material, and that cuttings bearing flower buds indicate low potential in rooting and general development.

New light on the kind of shoot that provides the most vigorous cuttings comes from work at the East Malling Research Station on the propagation of apple root stocks, and subsequently extended to stocks for budded rubber.[11, 12] Rooting capacity is inversely related to maturity. This applies not only to the individual shoots on a mother-plant but to the mother-plant itself. Applied practically this means that shoots used for cuttings should be those arising from a hard pruning, which stimulates rapid growth. Moreover, it is better to use relatively young bushes as a source of material. This implies that multiplication plots should be progressively laid down so that bushes older than five to seven years need not be used for cuttings. The maturer multiplication plots then become integrated with commercial fields. According to this criterion, the previously recognized superiority of green wood cuttings over red wood and the unsuitability of shoots with grey bark are accounted for. The apparent anomaly that arises from the fact that the terminal flexible portion of a shoot has a high mortality is due to the delicacy of the tissues which are liable to be damaged by the onset of even slightly unfavourable conditions. If carefully nursed they are the best rooters, but in practice are best discarded in large-scale projects.

A single-node cutting in the best of circumstances is a delicate object, handicapped in maintaining an adequate water balance and in photosynthetic activity: it needs careful handling. The surgery involved in making cuttings should be done with a sharp knife so as to minimize damage to conducting tissues: secateurs are unsuitable. Immediate transference to the propagating bed is desirable. If this is impossible, the Ceylon system of dropping the cuttings into water to maintain turgidity is helpful. Once safely installed in the propagation bed the interrelated factors of shade and moisture control are the critical ones in determining successful performance.

The materials used for the provision of shade are many and varied, for example, plastic cloches, bamboo slats, coir mesh, coconut fronds, grass and fern. Low shade of the cold frame type is inferior to shade at a height of five to six feet. Visser[10] puts the tolerable light limits at 25 per cent in the early stages of propagation and up to 50 per cent once rooting is in progress, till the hardening-off required before transplanting calls for gradual shade reduction.

The regulation of favourable moisture conditions both in the rooting medium and in the ambient air is not amenable to any neat formula for either shade or watering regime. Visser estimates the daily need of water to be 0·25–0·4 inch during dry sunny periods. With mist sprays the quantity is halved. Frequent watering can, in the writer's experience, be disastrous in unskilled hands. The best compromise appears to be that recommended by Goodchild,[13] a

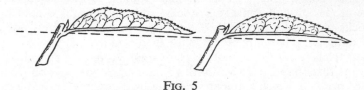

FIG. 5
Method of insertion of vegetative cuttings in propagating bed.

thorough drenching every two or three days supplemented daily by a light spraying of the foliage as a stabilizer of atmospheric humidity.

A successful watering technique demands good soil conditions in the propagation beds. A fairly valid generalization is that red soils are better than black ones. In Africa this distinction is absolute because black soils are unsuitable both in structure and soil reaction. Low pH values (4·5), well below the accepted level for tea culture in general, are advantageous and good crumb structure is conducive to good drainage, which is essential.

Such a soil in Ceylon is produced by the cultivation of Guatemala grass (*Tripsacum laxum*) for several years, and in all probability grassland soils of other species, e.g. *Pennisetum purpureum*, would be equally satisfactory. Soils long under tea cultivation are harmful. Visser, unable to find valid correlations with structure, pH or pathological agencies, suspects that such soils contain an undefined toxic principle. Soils of rich fertility are not conducive to good rooting performance. Mixtures of soil, sand and peat have no specially favourable feature and the inclusion of coir dust in any rooting medium has a bad effect.

Experience with growth-regulating substances confirms the conclusion that, as with other species, rooting is accelerated but these preparations do nothing to overcome the resistance some strains show to free rooting.

The procedure for establishing propagation nurseries is similar to that used for seed nurseries. The propagating bed should be firm and the stem of the cutting should be inserted at a slight angle to the perpendicular so that the leaf is near but not on the soil and is not damaged or detached by wind movement. Leaves should not overlap and are best arranged on a N.–S. axis. When the axiliary shoot has developed five leaves, the excision of the mother-leaf has no deleterious effect on either rooting or general development.

When roots are visible, development is enhanced by removing the cuttings to a less restricting environment at a time when this can be carried out without root damage. As with seedlings, transference to polythene pots can be made at this stage or they may be replanted in beds. Removal from beds when mature enough to be planted out in the field is best done with some form of transplanter which will preserve the adherent soil; or they may be allowed to grow large enough for "stumping". Goodchild[4] had considerable success with this method which obviates the transference of large quantities of soil, a formidable problem when, in new planting, as opposed to supplying programmes, millions of plants have to be moved.

REFERENCES

1. *Tea Encyclopaedia*, Tocklai Experimental Station, Indian Tea Association.
2. LEACH, R., *Tea Seed Management*, Bulletin No. 14 (New Series), Dept. of Agriculture, Nyasaland, 1936.
3. EDEN, T., *Tea Nursery Technique*, Tea Research Institute of East Africa, Pamphlet No. 4, 1953.
4. Tea Research Institute of East Africa, Annual Report, 1953, 19.
5. KEHL, F., *Tea Quarterly*, 1950, **21**, 3, T.R.I., Ceylon.
6. EDEN, T., ibid., 1941, **14**, 98, T.R.I., Ceylon.
7. TUBBS, F. R., ibid., 1946–7, **18**, 59, 91, T.R.I., Ceylon.
8. WIGHT, W., *Selection and Propagation of the Tea Plant*, Indian Tea Association Memorandum No. 15, 1942.
9. WIGHT, W., *Two and a Bud*, Newsletter, Indian Tea Association, 1961, **8** (1), 9.
10. VISSER, T., *et al.*, *Propagation of Tea Cuttings*, Bulletin No. 1 (New Series), 1959. Tea Research Institute of Ceylon.
11. GARNER, R. J., and HATCHER, E. S. J., Report, 14th International Horticultural Congress, Netherlands, 1955, 204.
12. TINLEY, G. H., and GARNER, R. J., *Nature*, 1960, **186**, 407.
13. GOODCHILD, N. A., Tea Research Institute of East Africa, Pamphlet, No. 15, 1958.
14. GREEN, M. J., Tea Research Institute of East Africa, Pamphlet, No. 20, 1964.

Chapter V

PREPARATION OF LAND AND PLANTING

Soil Conservation—Density of Planting—Planting Operations—Time of Planting—Shading and Weeding—Bush Formation.

THE three most important aspects in the preparation of land for tea planting are (1) adequate protection from soil erosion, (2) good preliminary cultivation to assist root development and weed suppression, (3) shade to protect both the soil and the young developing plant. These desirable features are not always easy to procure. Bad planting methods were more common in the earlier days of enterprise but they are by no means extinct at the present time. On smallholdings, where supervision difficulties are least, the cause is generally financial stringency. On large acreages, where difficulty in maintaining close supervision is increased, the further hazard arises of completing the specified acreage within the favourable planting season. The degree to which these difficulties become important and consequently harmful varies according to local conditions. Broadly speaking they are augmented by a very common lack of foresight. It is the writer's conviction that as much as three years of grace are frequently needed before the actual planting operations are put in hand if all the needful precautions are to be taken against poor planting stock, inadequately opened land, soil erosion, drainage and shade deficiency.

SOIL CONSERVATION

The old-fashioned procedure of starting all operations with a burn is little short of criminal because of the destruction of potential fertility that it involves. In forest land there were in the past mitigating circumstances, but with modern mechanical equipment anything in the nature of a general burn should be unnecessary. The burning of uprooted boles and roots is best carried out where the accumulated ash will not interfere with the immediate planting or, if this is impossible, should be followed by careful spreading of the ash: otherwise local patches of high soil reaction may bring disastrous consequences to the initial planting. When planting grassland, burning should be completely ruled out.

After clearing, cultivation for weed eradication should be put in hand as early as possible and particular attention paid to grasses of the couch-grass habit with stoloniferous roots. In East Africa particularly, a very vicious problem has been created because this operation has been neglected.[1] At this stage, bare fallowing and weeding introduces grave danger of soil erosion, and a cover crop, which will allow of cultivation and at the same time have a smothering effect, is urgently required. There is a choice of types. Bush green manures, maize or oats all have their place according to soil characteristics and climates; and where possible the crops should be lined to give room for inter-row cultivation. In old established tea, as far as records go, nothing of this kind ever received attention.

Before planting, the major concern should be with soil conservation works. The easy method of planting tea in straight lines up and down the hill has depreciated the value of land by erosion to an extent that it would be hard to exaggerate.[2] To repair the fault is difficult and much more trouble than to make the initial provision. With what limited success and at what cost such a transformation can be carried out is to be seen in Darjeeling where, by a system of revetting, small groups of bushes, or even individual plants, were protected by a terrace, and forest soil transported to build up the system.[3] There are various alternative ways of ensuring soil protection. The best is undoubtedly the skilled construction of narrow bench terraces as is mechanically done on land of more than a 16 degree slope in Kenya. Not every potential tea-growing region can provide expanses of land of comparatively easy contour that allows of this type of work. Machinery capable of working on gradients up to 30 degrees with ease and rapidity would be of great usefulness.

Contour planting of tea itself is a second suitable method more particularly applicable to terrain that cannot be mechanically terraced. For full efficiency the spacing should be close along the contour so that a real barrier to soil and water movement is provided by the interlacing of root and branches. Distances varying between two and two and a half feet are efficient in this respect.[4, 5]

Some soils are so relatively impermeable that intricate drainage is necessary in order to prevent standing water or wash-away of terrace bunds. This complicates terracing but is not an insuperable difficulty. A further variant is the contour drain protected by a raised bund on the upper side; the drain fills by seepage and, when properly constructed, wash-away of the bund is an inconsiderable danger.

Where drains are needed to carry off surplus water during heavy rainfall, they should be of the minimal slope consistent with their function and never more than 1 in 100. Calculations derived from the laws relating to the movement of water in earth channels show that in the past most gradient drains have been constructed with an incline greater than is needed to remove storm rain expeditiously and, by encouraging scour, add to, rather than detract from, the erosion problem. Wherever such open-gradient drains are used they should contain their own protection devices in the form of cross bunds, with a clearance for water movement, that turn them into a continuous series of silt pits.

The conversion of existing open drains on old tea land is a difficult and costly operation. Where the texture and structure of the soil are stable enough to allow of deepening the drains, without risk of the sides caving in, the best system is that of the reverse-slope drain which secured the approval of the Committee on Soil Erosion set up in Ceylon in 1930.[6] This method converts the bed of the drain into a saw-edged pattern of steps with vertical faces and gently sloping treads which run counter to the general slope of the drain. The reverse-slope is excavated in units of about fifteen feet. It is not so efficient as the normal bunded drain because it holds up less wash and is liable to continual erosion, at the edge of each step, unless protected by a stone facing or a grass sod. Nevertheless it has made a valuable contribution to soil conservation on thousands of acres in Ceylon which would otherwise have been quite devoid of protection.

Silt-pitted drains not only dispose of unabsorbed rain but also, in times of moderate rainfall between dry spells, immobilize rain and eroded soil which would otherwise be lost including, on land in a state of high cultivation, nutrient elements provided by fertilizer application.

Cover crops, though presenting some difficulties, protect newly-opened land against erosion at a critical time. They also help the decomposition of the disturbed natural herbage, and compete with unwanted and rejuvenating grasses. At a later stage, bush types give a measure of shade and wind protection which is very desirable provided that adequate control is exercised against the possibility of competition with the young tea for available moisture.

For this purpose both leguminous and non-leguminous species have been used with success. As low cover, *Polygonum nepalense* and two *Oxalis* species, *O. latifolia* and *O. corymbosa*, which are found in Ceylon, S. India and E. Africa, are of considerable value, the latter being especially suitable because they die down in dry weather and regenerate quickly from their bulbs at the onset of the rains. As nurse crops planted between rows of young tea Crotalarias, lupins and buck wheat *Fagopyrum esculentum* are widely used.

Grass strips used as erosion barriers can easily get out of hand and do considerable damage to adjacent tea. An exception is Khus Khus grass, *Vetiveria zizanioides*, a tussock grass reasonably restricted in root range. It needs to be controlled by periodical cutting.

DENSITY OF PLANTING

Closeness of planting is an important determinant of yield per acre. Cotton and groundnuts are noteworthy examples of crops that have given increased yields when densely planted. Contour planting of tea has led to larger populations per acre and experience, both experimental and practical, has shown that former norms of 2,000–3,000 bushes per acre were uneconomic.[11] Holliday,[7] studying the yield-population factor of vegetative crops, found the simple linear relationship between the density of stand and the average yield per acre to be

$$\frac{1}{y} = a + bx$$

where y is the yield per acre, x is the number of plants per acre and b is the regression coefficient, which expresses the proportionality of the yield increment in relation to the spacing of the plant. This factor varies according to cultural conditions and from crop to crop. The independent constant a reflects the influence of factors not associated with spacing, e.g. the upward growth.

Laycock,[8] using this relationship on tea yields, has found it to answer well irrespective of the age of the tea, its pattern of planting or country of origin. Fig. 6 shows the yield curves of plants of different ages and at different densities of planting. Amalgamating data of this type from Malawi, Assam and Indonesia, and expressing the results as a percentage of that produced by the 2,720 bushes per acre given by the 5-foot by 4-foot rectangular planting pattern, the predictable yields are as follows:

Plants per acre (Thousands)	1	2	2·7	3	4	5	6	7	8
% Yield	71	92	**100**	102	108	112	115	117	119

As Laycock indicates, these data and the curves of Fig. 6 show that there is no *optimum* density of planting. There is a ceiling beyond which closer planting does not increase yield. The law of diminishing returns works as inexorably in respect of spacing as of fertilizer applications.

Further consideration of these results prompts a number of queries. All the tea was relatively young, varying from six to fifteen years. It is sometimes suggested that the benefit of close planting is a feature of early years but that, in maturity with a complete cover, yields of all the more usual spacings even out. Hadfield[9] suggests that one important levelling factor is the shade effect of close-set foliage which diminishes the photosynthetic activity of leaves at a lower level. Laycock's curves do not substantiate this.

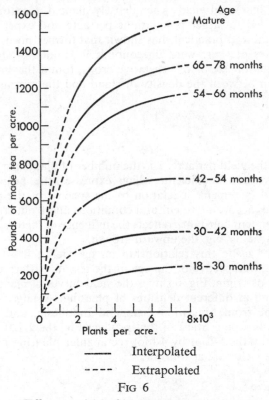

        ————— Interpolated

        - - - - Extrapolated

Fig 6

Effect on yield of plant density and age.

A point of considerable interest technically and economically is whether close planting demands higher fertilizer applications. Laycock finds no indication of an interaction (in the statistical sense of the word) between amount of nitrogen applied and density in planting, that is, the nitrogen is uniformly effective in all the spacing patterns under trial.

15. Profile of typical Ceylon tea soil

16. Opening bracken-land for tea in Kenya

17. Preparation of single-row bench-terraces, Darjeeling

18. Mixed shade trees, Indonesia

19. A 'bheti' nursery plant prepared for planting

20. Frame formation, first cut

21. Frame formation, second cut

22. Tipping at plucking-table level

The most persistently discussed hazard that high-density planting might disclose is that of inadequate moisture resources. The water storage capacity of soil at field capacity is limited. Does increased crop density make greater inroads into those resources, and if so what are the risks of trouble in prolonged dry weather? Penman's[10] researches into agricultural meteorology indicate that this risk can be discounted. His investigations show that the water used by different crops grown side by side, and therefore exposed to the same weather, is largely independent of the kind of crop, provided that the crop cover is complete or nearly so; that the crops are uniformly spaced and about the same height, and that adequate water is available. Expressed in another way, since transpiration uses the sun's radiant energy falling on the transpiring surface of the foliage, it is the extent of this surface that is important and not the number of plants from which it is derived. If the water supply dries up, then of course, closely planted tea will wilt, in common with other tea carrying equivalent foliage. Furthermore the argument does not apply to young tea not yet mature in root range and canopy. It is significant that in the drought of 1957 in Malawi the mature areas of tea with developed canopies fared better than immature clearings.

There are problems of management to be faced when close planting is adopted. If close planting in a contour row is to some extent compensated by wider spacing between rows a tiresome weed problem can be created until a spreading canopy has been established. Cultural operations in high-density planting are not necessarily more difficult or more expensive. Laycock's trials show that the normal 2,720 per acre density took three times as long to prune as one with 7,260 bushes per acre.

PLANTING OPERATIONS

For outstanding success, tea should be planted with all the care and refinement of a horticultural operation. For a variety of reasons, economic, climatic and, above all, human, such meticulous treatment cannot be given, but the closer to the horticultural norm the procedure keeps, the better the results that may be expected. In the previous chapter the importance of good planting material was emphasized whether the plant is raised from seed or vegetatively propagated cuttings. It is inherent in the cultivation of every crop that the benefit of good stock, genetically speaking, cannot be realized under poor cultural conditions. The quality of the work done at the initial planting operation can, and frequently does, determine the development of the tea bush throughout its economic lifetime.[12]

The first requirement is a planting hole of adequate size. Though a crowbar or a stout stick will make a hole large enough to take the tapering tap-root of a tea nursery stump, this type of planting, which still occasionally persists, is unsatisfactory for several reasons. The rotation of the implement compacts the walls of the hole and the developing roots become "pot-bound," especially if the soil is in a plastic condition of moisture-content and texture at the time of holing. Road excavations frequently reveal the inhibited development of roots resulting from this practice. In addition, and at the other extreme, the soil poured into such holes cannot be easily made firm to the degree that is desirable, with the consequence that air-pockets frequently form and the roots dry out and die. The size of hole required depends on the consistency of the soil, but a diameter of twelve inches and a depth of eighteen should be regarded as minimal and these dimensions can be increased with advantage in all but the most easily worked soils. The actual digging operation sometimes denatures the crumb structure of the surface layer, making it temporarily impervious to the passage of soil moisture. By leaving the holes open for a time this condition rights itself owing to the alternate wetting and drying of the puddled surface. The one drawback to allowing an interval to elapse between digging a hole and refilling it is the risk of losing the excavated soil by erosion. A decision on this point is a matter calling for knowledge of local conditions.

With the closer-spaced planting that is beginning to find favour, an economical alternative to holing is the excavation of a trench which gives a larger volume of cultivated soil for root expansion. Tubbs[13] found that in the relatively water-stable soil that is typical of Ceylon up-country districts, the presumably beneficial effect of this trenching, more particularly between bushes in the row, was still detectable in measurements of soil compactness, after eight years. It really matters little how the initial cultivation for planting is done provided it is efficient in both extent and quality. Tubbs' experiment was carried out on an area from which badly planted unthrifty tea had been removed. He further showed that, given proper cultivation, tea would grow well on the site, and that the soil disturbance caused by uprooting the old tea contributed largely to the beneficial results.

The ramming of earth into the hole in order to anchor the young plant is inimical to rapid growth of roots, but a reasonable density is required so that the roots shall be in intimate contact with moist soil. A young tea plant is well planted if it needs a definite effort to pull it out, and when there is a small excess of earth remaining above the natural level of the surrounding soil.

The actual level of planting is important. It is advantageous to plant at a level of half an inch lower than nursery level. In this manner the base of the stem will be protected from scorch, and buds be kept alive that would otherwise be liable to dry out. Protection of this kind, either from excess soil from the hole, or from a low planting level, is subject to abuse and, if overdone, may lead to serious trouble in areas troubled by infestation by termites.

At planting-out the use of artificial fertilizers is apt to be wasteful, except in localities where tea yellows disease is prevalent, because initial growth is more dependent on the elaborated food reserves of the plant than on mineral nutrition from the soil. This is particularly true of plants growing from stumps. Leaf litter, compost or bulk manure are a valuable help in securing good soil conditions in the immediate vicinity of the young roots, but they must be carefully used. An unmixed layer of compost at the bottom of a hole is a potent cause of water-logging which brings about shallow and mal-formed roots. Too high a concentration of mineralizing organic matter can locally produce such a high pH as to affect seriously the health of the root system.

TIME OF PLANTING

Tea in no way differs from other cultivated crops in responding favourably to meticulous care in the period immediately following planting. It is obviously impossible to specify in detail the most favourable seasons for a crop grown under such divergent geographical and climatic conditions. In countries having two rainfall peaks per annum it is possible to plant tea successfully over the greater part of the year. The south-western slopes of the mountain massif in Ceylon receive rain from both the S.-W. and N.-E. monsoons though in the former precipitation is both heavier and more persistent. As the dry period of the year is normally of short duration, usually no more than three months at the beginning of the year, both monsoon seasons can be used, though the S.-W. monsoon season is preferred. Where, as has previously been remarked, there is a controlling rain shadow, causing only one rainy season followed by a six months' drought, the rainy season is the only possible time for planting and supplying operations. The same rule holds good for regions where latitude influences the climatic cycle as in Tanganyika and Malawi. An exception is evident in Assam where the winter season of low rainfall, but abundant mist, is more successful than planting in the rains of mid-year. The one condition that appears to govern success is that the young plant should have the longest possible time to grow and establish itself before the arrival of the less favourable season. Assam winters provide sufficient moisture in the soil and a sufficiently temperate climate to satisfy the needs of a plant bearing little foliage.

Planted in the winter, they are sufficiently developed to withstand the rigours of the next winter season: planted in the summer, this is not invariably the case. In all circumstances early planting in the season is advisable before the soil and air temperatures have fallen to a low level that inhibits growth.

SHADING AND WEEDING

Winter planting in Assam can be carried out without immediately providing protective shade. In equatorial latitudes, however, this is essential. Fortunate climatic conditions may obviate damage to young unshaded plants for periods of days or even weeks, but a break of even a day or two in rainy or cloudy weather may cause enough sun-scorch to lessen the viability of buds, and any prolonged sunny spell is liable to bring splitting of stumps and permanent drying out. As a counsel of perfection shade protection should follow closely the planting operation. In practice this entails artificial shade constructed from bracken or grasses formed into a hood over the developing plant. It can usefully be supplemented by live shade in the form of bush green-manure plants trimmed to form an umbrella shade in regions of adequate rainfall. In Assam *Tephrosia candida* has been widely used for a period of two to three years in this way. In localities with long dry periods this method can be dangerous because of the excessive drain on soil moisture resources made by the nurse crop.

The preparation of land for planting invariably causes the germination over a short period of myriads of soft annual weeds. In the early stages succeeding the planting of tea, these weeds are, on balance, a favourable factor in protecting the young plants; but with approaching dry weather their systematic removal is of paramount importance.

Keen has expressed the consensus of agricultural opinion that weeds prevalent at an early stage of crop growth have a deleterious effect of a lasting character much more rigorous than the same weed density would occasion at a later stage of growth. He has also shown that fallow soils become self-mulched as the upper layers dry out, so that, even in severe droughts, moisture can generally be found at a depth of one to two feet. In the presence of actively growing weeds the field moisture reserve is rapidly drawn on and can be depleted for several feet, to the inevitable detriment of young plants with sparse root systems confined to superficial soil layers.

BUSH FORMATION

The procedure followed, when a young plant is established in the field, in order to form a bush of spreading habit and of convenient height for plucking, consists of subjecting the bush to various pruning operations interspersed with periods of growth. Since frame formation is a primary operation it is convenient to deal with it here, leaving the general question of routine pruning till a later chapter.

Broadly speaking three main methods can be distinguished. Of these methods (1) and (2) are found in Assam, with increasing emphasis on the first, whilst local variants of (2) and (3) are prevalent in Ceylon and East Africa and other regions where routine pruning is carried out at intervals of years and not annually as in Assam.

(1) The favoured Assam method consists of allowing the bush to grow for as long as three years, during which time it produces strong leaders and laterals, and then to cut across at 18 inches; removing at the same time the strong branches showing vigorous apical growth by cutting them down to the level at which branching starts. This operation is commonly referred to as centring. Tea thus treated is then allowed to regenerate till the bush is some 27 inches high, and then can be brought into bearing by light plucking. This system gives an early return of crop, and, given adequate branching in the first place, produces a satisfactory frame.

(2) A better spaced and controlled frame can be encouraged by the second method. This entails leaving the bush till it is 3 to 5 feet high and then cutting back the entire growth to within 4 to 6 inches of the ground. The arguments in favour of this treatment are twofold; first, that it allows the root system to become well established before drastic treatment, and second, that it promotes low spread and more branches than the centring method. Whilst both these contentions carry weight, the method involves severe loss of time before a bush can be brought into production, and the cut, being made into wood of considerable size, is unlikely to be occluded by new growth, or even to callus-over in its entirety. A great deal of growth is made which, apart from contributing to root storage reserves, is of no further use and is discarded. Tubbs[14] has tabulated results showing the quantities of prunings discarded in two experiments where cuts were made at 4 and 8 inches respectively, in different localities, on bushes at various heights between 2 and 6 feet. The high degree of wastage is apparent. Cutting at this low level involves further pruning operations later, each designed to develop the outward spread of the bush.

(3) The object in this method is to secure a low branching frame without the attendant disadvantages of the previous method. The first cut is made early when the branches at cutting height are no more than pencil thickness, and the height of the cut is determined by

the character of the growth at the time. A large number of young plants will usually be found to have only one stem, and these are cut at about 6 inches with some attention to the near presence of a viable bud. Plants with double stems at, or below, 6 inches, are cut higher (8 inches) and multiple-stemmed plants as high as 10 inches. After regeneration further cuts at 12 to 16 inches are made according to the configuration of the frame. Thereafter the bushes are brought into bearing with a plucking table not less than 2 feet high. This earlier and less drastic pruning encourages occlusion and healing of wounds to a considerable extent and involves less waste of time and growth. It succeeds in relatively dry climates where a large bulk of foliage on untreated plants periodically causes drought-inflicted die-back. The more detailed procedure as carried out in East Africa on the recommendation of the Tea Research Institute is described by Eden.[12] By following some such method bushes are trained to a good shape and are never, even on long pruning cycles, at such a height that the plucking table is out of reach of the pluckers. An ideal build-up would bring a bush at the end of a normal cycle to 50 inches, as set out in the following schedule.

					Inches
Frame	..	..	..	..	16
Tipping	..	..	..	..	10
4 years' plucking increment			..		24
					50

Thereafter, except for reasons of accidental damage, there should be no need to prune below the sixteen-inch level, producing thereby infectible wounds and snags on the primary branches.

REFERENCES

1. EDEN, T., *Tropical Agriculture*, 1954, **31**, 112.
2. *Report of Soil Erosion Committee*, Sessional Paper No. 3, Government Printer, Colombo, Ceylon, 1931.
3. EDEN, T., *Report on a Visit to the Tea Districts of North-East India*, Tea Research Institute of Ceylon, Bulletin 14, 1936.
4. DANIEL, F. C., *Tea Quarterly*, 1951, **21**, 1.
5. GLOVER, P. M., *Hedge Planting of Tea*, Indian Tea Association, Memorandum No. 21, 1949.
6. NORRIS, R. V. and EDEN, T., *Tea Quarterly*, 1930, **3**, 4.
7. HOLLIDAY, R., *Nature*, 1960, **186**, 22.
8. LAYCOCK, D. H., *Tropical Agriculture*, 1961, **38**, 195.
9. HADFIELD, W., *Two and a Bud*, Indian Tea Association, 1963, **10** (No. 4) 9.

10. PENMAN, H. L., *Water Control for increased Production, The Biological Productivity of Britain*, Institute of Biology, 1958.
11. VAN ROGGEN, M. A., *Archief v.d. Thee Cultuur*, 1948, **16**, 25.
12. EDEN, T., *The Establishment of Young Tea*, Tea Research Institute of East Africa, Pamphlet No. 9, 1954.
13. TUBBS, F. R., *Emp. J. exp. Agric.*, 1947, **15**, 160.
14. TUBBS, F. R., *Investigations on the Planting, Pruning and Plucking of the Tea Bush*, Tea Research Institute of Ceylon, Bulletin No. 15, 1936.

Chapter VI

PRUNING AND PLUCKING

Pruning Objectives—Balance of Growth—Carbohydrate Economy—Pruning Cycle Patterns—Types of Pruning— Time of Pruning—Regeneration from Pruning—Plucking Systems—Standards of Plucking—Mechanical Plucking.

In the course of the perennial growth of tea there is a continual removal of the vegetative organs of the plant, at short intervals by the process of plucking, and at long intervals by pruning. The two aspects are so intimately connected that they are best dealt with together.

PRUNING OBJECTIVES

Whereas the annual plant has two well-marked and successive stages of development, the vegetative and the reproductive, evergreen perennials start with a vegetative phase and ultimately have superimposed on this the production of flowers and fruit. Thereafter, unless artificially controlled, the vegetative and reproductive phases proceed side by side, the former continuously, the latter according to the seasonal rhythm. For tea production the reproductive phase is redundant, and the art or science of bush management is directed towards keeping the plant continuously in the vegetative phase. The paramount operation for this purpose is pruning. On a broad view it is the most important cultural operation in commercial tea production, and is the most fraught with consequences for good or ill. Pruning is still more of an art than a science, because the physiology of the tea bush is still very imperfectly understood. The individuality of each bush, combined with the corresponding individuality of the person who shall prune it, make experimentation most difficult. All that can be attempted in this chapter is to systematize the conceptions that lie behind various stages of pruning in the light of the relatively simple experiments that have been carried out, and of planting experience in general. There is no single aspect of tea cultivation that is so controversial as that of pruning.

The objects of pruning are briefly as follows:

48

23. Annual top-pruning (Assam)

24. Tea pruned and plucked on the slope

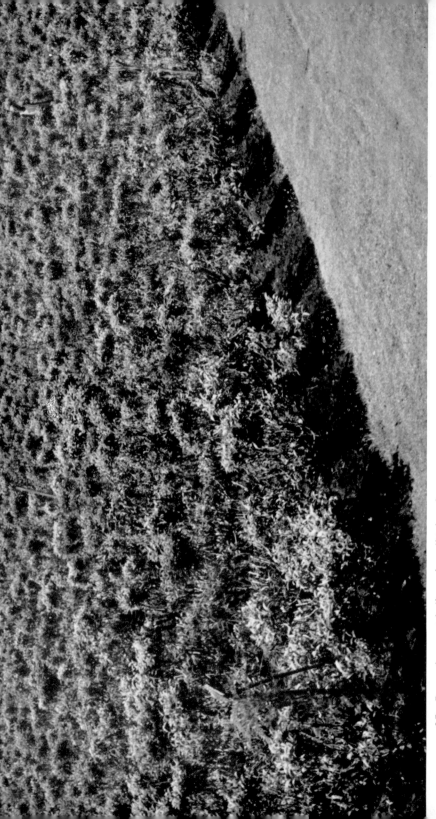

25. Pruned tea with 'lungs' or 'kickers'

(1) To maintain the plant permanently in the vegetative phase.

(2) To stimulate, in particular, the young shoots that constitute the cropped portion of the bush.

(3) To form as extensive a frame as possible in two dimensions, on which in the third dimension, the "flush" will rapidly and continuously regenerate.

(4) To keep the height of the bush within the bounds of easy and efficient plucking.

(5) To renew the actively growing branches so that replacement of healthy wood and foliage keeps pace with the ravages of death or damage; to maintain a sufficient volume of mature foliage to meet the physiological needs of the plant, and to promote rapid renewal of flush suitable for manufacture into tea of quality.

Tubbs[1] has emphasized the conception that plants, like soil, are subject to depreciation, and skill in pruning is the chief means whereby the inevitable depreciation of a long-term perennial can be checked, if given proper attention. Although every form of pruning puts a check on immediate growth, the fundamental characteristic is the imparting of a stimulus. In common parlance, pruning is often referred to as a shock to the bush, but this anthropomorphic conception, based on the analogy of what happens to man and animals when their individual organs are damaged, is entirely false. The persistence of the fallacy is the more surprising since the stimulative effect of plucking is widely recognized. Bad pruning, if persisted in, can and does frequently cause local or entire death to a tea bush; but this is attributable to ordinary physiological effects quite other than that of shock.

BALANCE OF GROWTH

Whilst the tea plant must always be regarded as a whole organism, the recurrent checks and stimuli that pruning and plucking impart to different parts have a profound effect on the growth of the individual parts. Eden[2, 3] has shown that, under a uniform system of pruning and plucking, an extraneous stimulus, such as manuring, affects the growth of wood, foliage and crop proportionately. A nutritive stimulus, in other words, does not produce crop at the expense of permanent foliage or wood (Fig. 7). He further showed that in a settled cultural system the crop produced bore a reasonably constant relationship to the amount of foliage carried by the bush at the end of its pruning cycle. On the other hand, by altering styles of plucking the proportions of crop, foliage and wood are radically altered. These aspects of tea culture will be dealt with in detail later; they are mentioned here because it is essential for a full understanding of pruning and plucking to realize that these operations affect the whole economy of the bush in regard to its growth, nutrition and accumulation of reserves.

The balance between leaf that is removed as crop and what is retained as maintenance foliage is an artificial one created at will. The young leaf is the most active in synthesizing elaborated foodstuffs: the *real* foodstuffs of the plant, as distinct from the nutritive

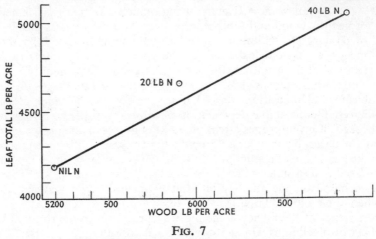

FIG. 7

Correlation between growth of leaf and wood

elements absorbed by the roots. It is constantly being removed with important consequences to reserves. Old leaves are less photosynthetically active than young ones. A system of pruning, which diminishes the constant renewal of new shoots from the lower regions of the frame, whilst encouraging, temporarily, the growth of flush, can do untold damage to the productive capacity of the bush in the long run. Any consideration therefore of pruning must include a survey of its effect on the metabolism of the bush as a whole, and upon the maintenance of adequate reserves, since the pruning operation, in whole or in part, removes the active chemical laboratory of the plant.

CARBOHYDRATE ECONOMY

Healthy growth demands a sufficiency of those food constituents that produce energy and build up the tissues of the developing plant. The former comprise the carbohydrates and the latter, predominatingly, are partly carbohydrates and partly proteins. As far as storage is concerned, the carbohydrate reserve, which represents the excess of photosynthesized material built up in the leaves, and not immediately required for active growth, is localized in the roots of the plant where it is present as starch granules in the cells. The protein reserve on the other hand is found throughout the plant, and particularly in its green parts. By removing a large volume of leaf and young wood at pruning time, and bringing to a halt the synthesizing activities of the plant, the recovery from pruning is made mainly dependent on the mobilization of reserves in the roots. Gadd[4] was the first to point out that deaths of apparently healthy bushes, following pruning, were not, as had been previously supposed, due to pathological causes, but were due to the more or less entire absence of starch reserves in the roots. Tubbs[5] extended the observations and showed that both local environment and methods of pruning were determining factors.

Under the condition of continuous bearing of bushes without a completely dormant season, such as is common to all districts in Ceylon, Tubbs showed that there was a definite and linear relationship between the elevation at which tea was grown and the magnitude of its starch reserves; all other factors, such as age from pruning, being constant. The altitude factor controls the rate of growth of the plant, and its respiration losses, through temperature differences. At high altitudes starch reserves were sufficient for full recovery of bushes after pruning, even though they were clean-pruned, leaving no foliage at all. At lower elevations, decreasing carbohydrate reserves led to increased die-back, principally of peripheral branches. In severe cases the bush as a whole died. The lowest threshold of hydrolizable carbohydrate reserve, expressed as dextrose, was about 11 per cent of the total dry matter. For each thousand feet increase of elevation the average carbohydrate content increased by 2 per cent till, at an elevation of 6,500 ft. the value was 24 per cent. The appropriate linear equation was:

$$D = 11 \cdot 17 + 0 \cdot 20E$$

where D is carbohydrate content, expressed as dextrose, and E is elevation in thousands of feet. A similar survey for nitrogen showed no significant systematic variation at all, the corresponding function being:

$$N = 1 \cdot 065 - 0 \cdot 002E$$

where N is nitrogen content.

The practical application of this work is dealt with in a later section. In the present context it is necessary to say that experience shows that carbohydrate deficiency is not of particular severity in climates where tea has a definite resting period. The Assam valley, being out of the tropic zone, has a real winter period when growth stops gradually.

During such periods the carbohydrate reserves accumulate. Similar conditions exist in Southern Tanganyika which has also a cold dry season when growth declines, though cropping is not entirely suspended. An apparent exception to the relationship between altitude and carbohydrate reserves is found in Kenya. There, in a climate where temperatures are on a par with those in Ceylon districts in which carbohydrate deficiency is of no importance, the characteristic symptoms of die-back are frequently found. Eden explains this apparent discrepancy in behaviour as being associated with two ancillary factors. The first is the absence of dormant growth periods of any note in the Kericho district; the other is the substantial destruction of roots, and their contained reserves, by cultivation of the exceptionally vicious nature needed to eradicate couch grass.[6]

PRUNING CYCLE PATTERNS

The stimulus that pruning gives to the vegetative growth of tea wears off in the course of time and the renewal of the stimulus is the chief reason for pruning. The rate of decline is influenced by a variety of factors that are only imperfectly understood. Type of tea (jat), method of pruning, system of plucking and the natural fertility of the soil all play a part, so that the task of estimating the economic length of a pruning cycle is not easy. In order to co-ordinate work and crop production on an estate, a decision has to be made in advance, but that decision may be varied according to whether the field appears to be "run out" or not. In general, because of its slower growth, tea in more temperate climates runs longer pruning cycles than at tropical temperatures; with the proviso that this does not necessarily apply to situations which have a real wintering period.

Although the definition of pruning cycle periods has to be made on empiric grounds, the norm is set by the yield curve. Pruning is a necessary evil, not to be indulged without good cause, and certainly not to be put into operation at the first decline of crop. So long as the average yield to date is not declining, it is agriculturally sound practice to continue without interposing so drastic an operation as pruning. There may be other compelling reasons for pruning of which a frequently experienced example is high cost of plucking in later years, or acute shortage of labour.

Yield curves constructed plucking by plucking are too complicated in pattern to provide a criterion, but annual yields free from the grosser vagaries of climatic effect are distinctly instructive. Dating periods from the time of pruning, Eden[7] has shown that the yield patterns of individual fields, uniformly treated, are remarkably stable, and repeat themselves from one pruning cycle to another, even down to minor inflections in the curve. A study of large numbers of such cases reveals that they exhibit many gradations between two extremes. The first, which is designated the "early maximum," gives the highest yield in the year following pruning, and thereafter falls away sharply. The second, the "late maximum," gradually increases in yield till the curve becomes for all practical purposes asymptotic. The poorer jats of tea are usually of the first pattern, the better of the second. Young tea tends to follow the second pattern, but whether age is a true determinant is questionable because recent plantings have so frequently been confined to the better types. Styles of pruning also exert an influence to a lesser degree. Thus, Tubbs' experiments on pruning methods, which included a low clean-prune and a high cut-across, showed that both sets of plots conformed to the early maximum pattern though the peak was more pronounced with the harder pruning. Ample nutrition acts as a leveller.

The progressive weakening of the initial stimulus as time from pruning increases is shown by other characteristics besides yield. Tubbs found that size of leaf diminished and percentage of dormant buds (banjhi) increased with time, in accordance with a logarithmic relationship. In conjunction with Lamb he also detected changes in polyphenol (tannin) content which paralleled reports of superior quality in the manufactured teas.

TYPES OF PRUNING

Collar-Pruning

The severest type of pruning is collar-pruning, the bole of the bush being cut at or near ground level. When this drastic operation is undertaken the best chance of success is provided if the cut is slightly below the ground, in order that the wound can be covered with earth and the tissues protected against progressive die-back. Satisfactory recovery from collar-pruning is greatly influenced by carbohydrate reserves. Consequently the hazard is less in regions where tea has a long dormant period, as in Assam, and to a less degree in Malawi and Southern Tanganyika; or grows in a temperate climate. In these situations carbohydrate deficiency is not a problem. In times past, collar-pruning has been practised without undue risk in both Assam and Tanganyika. At the Tea Research Institue of Ceylon[17] a recent programme of rehabilitation of old tea, which involved a moderate proportion of collar-pruning, was successful and the casualties less than expected. With adequate manuring, this tea was yielding a thousand pounds per acre two and a half years after pruning.

Medium-Pruning

In this term may be included the once prevalent clean-pruning common in Ceylon and South India, and the occasional down-pruning operation in Assam. Continuous top-working, as practised

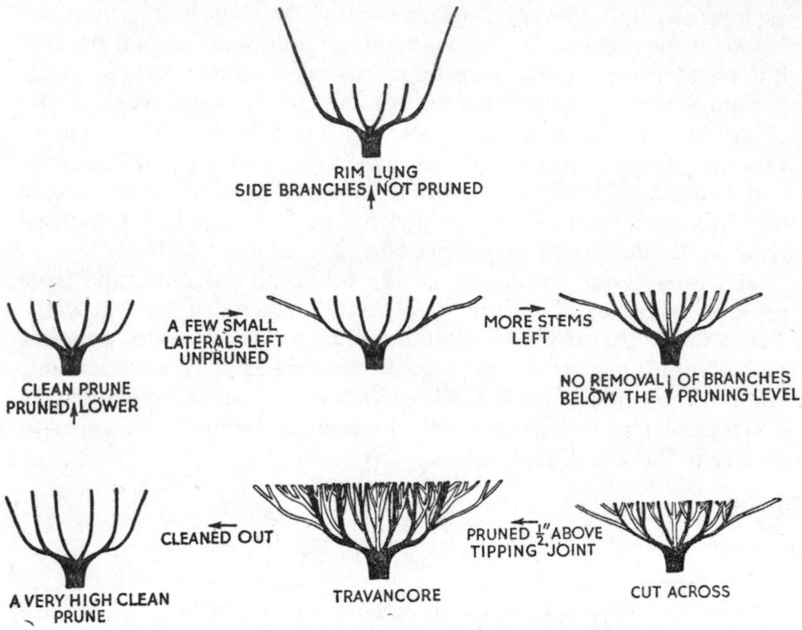

RIM LUNG
SIDE BRANCHES NOT PRUNED

A FEW SMALL
LATERALS LEFT
UNPRUNED

CLEAN PRUNE
PRUNED LOWER

MORE STEMS
LEFT

NO REMOVAL OF BRANCHES
BELOW THE PRUNING LEVEL

A VERY HIGH CLEAN
PRUNE

CLEANED OUT

TRAVANCORE

PRUNED ½" ABOVE
TIPPING JOINT

CUT ACROSS

FIG. 8
Types of Pruning

in the Assam Valley, gradually increases the height of a bush to an inconvenient degree. For this reason, and in order to stimulate new wood and a renewal of maintenance foliage at lower levels, top-pruning is interspersed at intervals of from twelve to eighteen years with a cut at 18 inches from the ground. In Ceylon, where annual top-pruning is virtually unknown, pruning of this type was the norm on tea of cycle lengths from three to five or six years until the advent of blister blight made lighter pruning imperative. Except occasionally, as exemplified in Assam, hard-pruning is to be deprecated. In a bush already debilitated it may bring about the exhaustion of already low reserves without producing a compensating quantity of new main-tenance foliage, with the result that, after as few as two operations of this type, the spread of the bush is seriously curtailed and its debilitated condition in no way improved: frequently just the con-trary. Many planters will claim pronounced success for the method and in individual instances this cannot be gainsaid. Hard-pruning will stimulate depth in canopy foliage, but if that is done at the ex-pense of spread the advantage is, more often than not, illusory. Severe pruning always brings in its train the danger of wound infec-tion. In a young plant, as a formative process, it is necessary; and in that state occlusion of wounds is more rapid and frequent. On old bearing bushes hard-pruning is not usually accompanied by such vigorous rejuvenation processes unless it is rested subsequently.

Top-Pruning
The standard for this method is that set by Assam. The height at which the cut is made depends on the previous history of the bush, rising from the datum height of a medium-pruning by intervals of an inch or less till an unmanageable height of bush in plucking brings about a recurrence of the harder pruning. In practice this style of pruning leaves a considerable amount of foliage-leaf on the bush, but in the Assam winter this residue eventually defoliates naturally. In non-wintering regions the foliage-leaf remains attached and con-tinues to perform its normal physiological function. Whatever the circumstances the initial process is a uniform cut-across followed by cleaning out of thin, diseased and obviously dormant shoots. In Assam, Cooper[8] showed that delay in this secondary operation had no effect on subsequent crop production in the following season. Elsewhere, in the regions marked by continuous cropping, it is customary to combine the two operations; or to follow closely with the second, using a gang of specially efficient pruners.

Fringe- or Lung-Pruning
The common feature of these closely allied methods is that whilst not deviating from the norm in the matter of severity of pruning (over the bush as a whole) they leave all leaf below the pruning level, including straggling branches near the base, and omit the cutting-back of some or all of the peripheral branches. These have been referred to as "lungs" but the term is a misnomer, since their function is in no way connected with respiration.

The previously quoted work of Gadd and Tubbs definitely estab-lished the fact that many bushes grown in forcing climates lived pre-cariously as regards elaborated foodstuffs, at the end of a pruning cycle. Under a system of clean-pruning they started a new cycle of development seriously, if not completely, devoid of mobilizable carbohydrate reserves. In order to contend with this condition the system of lung- or fringe-pruning was advocated. Thereby a sufficiency of actively synthesizing foliage was left on the bush to tide it over the critical interval before the balance between withdrawal and accumulation could be righted by normal development. The experimental evidence published by Tubbs[5] showed unequivocally that, not only was initial growth (before restarting the plucking process) benefited, but also that, at the lower elevations, the advantage was carried over to the subsequent cropping period, particularly in the early stages. The methods of lung-pruning, or variations involving a similar leaf-leaving principle, thus contributed to health and efficiency in two ways: they diminished the incidence of die-back and death in individual bushes; and in survivors they gave enhanced crops. By the same means the carbohydrate deficiency in the Kenya Highlands has proved amenable to treatment.

Skiffing

The lightest of all pruning systems is the skiff whereby the foliage is levelled off (sometimes no lower than the level of the last plucking), the cut being made in green stem, or, with a harder skiff, into young red wood. The reasons for pruning in this fashion are several. It may be desired to do no more than level a plucking-table that has got out of order and cannot easily be rectified by the normal process of breaking back individual shoots to the correct level. This state of affairs is likely to arise when cropping is vigorous and labour is short. Skiffing may be resorted to as a means of reducing the plucking task on an estate where the only alternative is to throw a field out of plucking and accept the inevitable rise in the plucking-table; a result that may bring its own difficulties. Or skiffing may be undertaken to reduce the bulk of foliage before permanent wilting supervenes in a drought. In both these circumstances skiffing fulfils a useful purpose from the viewpoint of management if not from that of agricultural suitability.

Skiffing is sometimes done in the hope of extending the pruning cycle as a matter of practical convenience, and of sustaining crop which would otherwise fall away. Cooper[8] has summarized experiments on skiffing and deprecates the suggestion that the gains are worth while. In perennially bearing tea the risks are considerable. After the inevitable check in cropping capacity a rapid and voluminous flush is not uncommon. If after a period of no more than a few months the tea then comes into normal pruning, it is not unlikely that recovery will be irregular and, in severe cases, the incidence of die-back great because the reduction in maintenance foliage, plus the stimulus to crop, has adversely affected the balance of carbohydrate reserves. Considering all the factors involved, skiffing must at best be regarded as a risky procedure not calculated to benefit the bush as a whole.

TIME OF PRUNING

In practice the distribution of labour compels estate managers to prune over an extended period unless, as in Assam, there is a definite wintering season when other works are not urgent, or are at a standstill. Cooper's findings in Assam have wide relevance. They are that the best time for pruning is during a dormant period. This is the time when food reserves are at their highest. In relation to what has been said about the carbohydrate economy of tea this dictum is logical. In Assam the application of this principle brings pruning into the winter season. Cooper has shown that pruning in the rains is disadvantageous. In Ceylon and East Africa the period immediately following the dry weather fits in best. In some situations dry-weather pruning, by reducing transpiration losses, protects the tea from the deaths that occur in a severe drought. On the other hand scorch may abort buds and even damage wood, with resultant die-back. If dry-weather pruning is contemplated, the period to put it into practice is at the early stage when growth has slowed down enough to create a favourable carbohydrate balance, and when there is still time for a protective canopy of leaves to grow and mature before the hottest period arrives. This procedure requires judgement and a considerable element of luck, but can be very successful.

The technique of pruning itself plays a significant part in ensuring good results, and neglect of elementary principles can vitally affect the subsequent development and health of the bush. The cut branch offers easy access to invading pathogenic fungi. A clean smooth cut that easily dries hampers infection. An oblique cut favours drainage of adherent moisture but increases the vulnerable area: the accepted compromise is at an angle of 45 degrees. As a matter of principle a cut should ideally be made as near as possible to a viable bud. A stem must die back as far as the first developing bud, and these residual snags are a potent source of infection by wood-rotting fungi. Moreover, if a bud springs close to the cut there is more active callus growth and, in favourable cases, actual occlusion of the wound. The counsel of perfection is to prune a branch to an outward eye and thus to secure these advantages and, in addition, promote the radial spread of the frame. In practice such niceties are well-nigh impossible, but when the buds do awake from dormancy it is highly desirable that a "sanitary" pruning should be carried out so as to remove snags. If saws are used they should be supplemented by sharp knives to pare the rough surface. Sharp implements are of the essence of good pruning. Secateurs should never be used. The best of them exert a crushing action which damages the regenerative cambial tissues, even if it does not split the stem. All cuts of large size should be protected by a fungicidal and waterproof paint of bituminous constituents. But even this protection is comparatively valueless unless it is renewed at intervals.

REGENERATION FROM PRUNING

The period immediately after pruning is one of unrestricted growth to allow the bush to produce new shoots which will eventually mature as branches, replacing those no longer serviceable by reason of breakage or disease. The developing shoots reclothe the bush with maintenance foliage upon which the metabolism of growth depends. Later the new shoots have to be organized into a regular plucking-table from which to pluck the flush. The manner of so doing varies according to circumstances. Where, as in Assam, there is a genuine winter dormancy, the spring growth is rapid and vigorous. By the time the new growth is uniform enough to be broken back leaving six inches of "tipping growth", the bush can be brought into plucking on regular rounds. Cooper[9] concluded from his experiments that six inches was the most suitable tipping level and that it was advantageous to leave a leaf above the fish-leaf, at the first round of plucking only, as a supplement to the maintenance foliage.

This system works well in East Africa where no dormant period occurs but where growth is profuse in comparison, for example, with Ceylon. In Ceylon the old-established tea has traditionally been treated more selectively. The tipping operation is extended over a longer period as shoots grow up to the required level. The tipping length is shorter and is conducive to the development of side shoots to fill up the leaf canopy. The question of balanced renewal of wood, maintenance foliage and flush has received much attention in Ceylon as will be related in the subsequent section.

There is another aspect of recovery from pruning that deserves attention. In the process of time the frame of a bush deteriorates by reason of accident, disease or lack of care in pruning. Such bushes become "passengers", and contribute little to the crop yield, as indicated previously (p. 31). The progress made in replanting long-established areas with clonal stocks has so far been slow. Clonal supplying and liberal manuring policies have postponed the evil day when yields will be stabilized or decline, as they must, unless replanting can be accelerated. Hazarding an estimate, until half of existing acreages is under clonal tea the future of the tea industry depends upon bushes of uncertain age, virility and yield potentiality. It is no more than common prudence to take steps to rehabilitate this old tea in so far as this is possible.

There comes a time when, whilst adhering to the maxim that pruning is a necessary evil, the emphasis has to be transferred from the word "evil" to the word "necessary". There is evidence that, avoiding indiscriminate collar-pruning, hard pruning, followed by a long period of rest, can rehabilitate a bush and, in the long run, more than compensate for loss of crop during the resting period. Certain necessary conditions must be observed. The standard of pruning must be high and large cuts must be protected by fungicidal dressings. Strong leaders should be cut back from time to time to encourage filling out the frame. Many of the cuts so made will occlude. When the hard pruning is instituted, care should be taken to ascertain that the carbohydrate reserves are satisfactory. The most propitious time is during a relatively dormant phase of growth. The period of rest can, according to circumstances, be one, two or even three years. Normal cultural operations should be carried out, including manuring.

PLUCKING SYSTEMS

The different ways in which an identical objective is reached in different countries is well illustrated by the dissimilar systems of plucking. To anyone used to the Assam system of plucking to the fish-leaf, the leaving of a single leaf above the fish-leaf at each plucking round, as was the custom in Ceylon, appeared to court a substantial loss of crop. To clarify the matter Eden[3] designed an experiment subsequently carried on by Portsmouth[10] and Visser[11] which extended over eighteen years. The spectacular and devastating results in the initial years led to modification of design and the ultimate pattern tested continuous plucking (a) to the single leaf (control), (b) to the fish-leaf and (c) a system of plucking, in alternate pruning cycles, by each method in turn. For convenience of exposition the treatments will be codified as follows. The letters S and F refer to yield periods when single or fish-leaf plucking respectively were in operation. The lower case letters s and f provide indications of the style of plucking in the preceding cycle. The four possible phases were therefore sS; fF; sF; and fS.

The results of this trial demonstrated that continuous plucking to the fish-leaf (fF) increased yields dramatically at first, but with falling efficiency, in comparison with continuous single-leaf plucking (sS). When the experiment had reached a settled state the average benefit from continuous fish-leaf plucking over three pruning cycles of three years was 7 per cent of the yield of the single leaf series. At the same time the weights of maintenance foliage and wood removed at pruning time were drastically reduced, falling to 32 per cent and 26 per cent respectively.

The alternating system gave slightly greater benefit than the continuous fish-leaf plucking (8 per cent). The maintenance foliage and wood were almost fully restored by reverting to single-leaf plucking after a cycle of the fish-leaf regime (foliage 96·5: wood 90·4).

It seems plain therefore that continuous fish-leaf plucking produces flush to the detriment of the foliage and wood. The fact that, despite this, flush is still produced in quantity suggests that the abundant head of foliage resulting from single-leaf plucking is possibly more than physiological efficiency requires. Visser[11] follows Hadfield[12] in supposing that for lack of light such foliage canopies are *ipso facto* less efficient than less dense ones. Visser was accordingly prompted to try shorter periods of alternating plucking regimes by making changes within a single cycle. The results were highly satisfactory. Plucking to a single leaf for sixteen months, approximately equally divided between the initial and the final months of a forty-six-month cycle, produced the highest yield and reduced foliage by only 5 per cent and wood by 33 per cent; the latter being half the loss brought about by continuous fish-leaf plucking. Inserting a resting period of six months at the end of the cycle completely safeguarded the starch reserves needed for recovery after pruning. Features which were not so favourable were that the flush size was diminished, and the proportion of banjhi shoots increased. These characteristics affect the manufacturing quality of the leaf. This investigation also demonstrated the drain on carbohydrate reserves during recovery from pruning and indicated that a period of between eight and thirteen months, according to circumstance, is required after pruning before the starch reserves are restored to normal levels.

STANDARDS OF PLUCKING

The length of time needed for the plucked shoot to redevelop a new shoot ready for plucking varies according to the plucking systems employed and according to nutrient and climatic conditions.

Intervals of between seventy and ninety days are representative.[13]
Right from the formation stage of tipping the rhythm of growth of
individual shoots varies so that at the plucking-table level there are
always shoots of varied maturity. Hand plucking enables mature

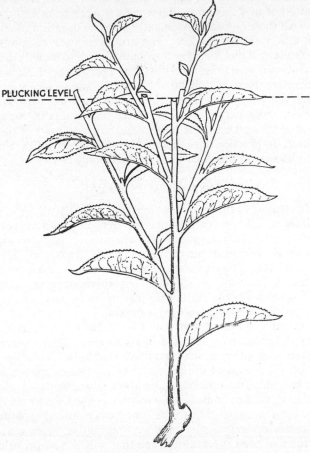

PLUCKING LEVEL

FIG. 9
A correctly plucked shoot of tea

shoots to be distinguished from immature, and ability to do this
quickly and with discrimination constitutes plucking skill (Fig. 9). The
actual intervals between plucking rounds must therefore be chosen so
that neither too many shoots, left from a previous plucking, have become overgrown, nor too few have developed in the meantime to make

plucking worth while. Ideally a tea bush could be plucked every day if expense were no object. Loss of crop is inevitable if leaf is left too long on the bush because, unless standards are lax, it is necessary to break back and discard extra leaves. Moreover a shoot more mature than desirable tends to dormancy, and in order to ensure the regular stimulation of new flush may have to be broken back and discarded *in toto*. All these considerations enter into the question of maintaining not only yield but quality. The problem of the relationship between standard of plucking (i.e. how many leaves to include in plucked flush) and quality of the manufactured tea will be dealt with in a later chapter. Here it will be sufficient to state categorically that chemical analysis in the laboratory, manufacturing experiments in pilot trials, and general experience in tea factories confirms the conclusion that the best tea is made from flush that consists of two leaves and a bud. In practice this standard is only imperfectly maintained, but its relevance to good tea production cannot be denied.

MECHANICAL PLUCKING

The harvesting of the crop is the most expensive of all the individual operations entailed in tea production. Wright[14] in a survey of the possibilities of mechanization of field operations in Ceylon attributes more than 44 per cent of the total cost to this item alone. It is therefore natural that attention should be paid to the development of a machine and, if possible, a technique that will reduce costs and harvest a flush capable of being made into tea that is as good as that traditionally plucked into the labourer's basket.

As regards commonwealth countries a start has been made by adapting the hedge-trimmer used by topiarists, with a motive power that consists of either a self-contained internal-combustion engine carried on the person of the operator, or an electric motor fed with current by cable from mobile generators conveniently deployed in the fields. In broken country such as that of the Ceylon tea districts a hand-borne machine of this type is probably the only solution, but in the more topographically favoured regions of Assam and East Africa the real need is for a machine that will be self-propelled and can negotiate the lines of tea bushes. Unfortunately the tea industry is of small size compared with that of grain farming, and the capital outlay needed for experiment and production of a prototype would be very heavy. Nonetheless, even if the solution of the problem is a long-term project entailing replanting tea in hedges sufficiently far apart to accommodate a traction unit, the possibilities cannot be lightly dismissed. If estate planting practice is to be modified to prepare for ventures of this nature, engineering research must also take cognizance of the fact that yield per acre of a crop is directly correlated with stand, and that there is a limit therefore to the accommodation of planting distances to the needs of mechanized implements.

As far as experiments have gone there are encouraging pointers to the feasibility of mechanical plucking. Much depends upon working out a technique of operation and on preparing the bush by suitable pruning. Fay's[15] preliminary work indicates that teas are favourably reported on and that leaf mechanically plucked is superior to the hand-plucked variety in respect of damage done by handling, because the clean cutting of flush is less detrimental than crushing. On properly prepared bushes the rhythm of growth is stabilized by mechanical harvesting with the result that the number of plucking rounds can be reduced. Yields obtained are comparable to those from hand plucking and, working strictly to a level as these machines do, the spreading capacity of the bush is encouraged. Self-propelled machines have been constructed in Russia[16] and Assam.[13] In all the trials reported, the essential conditions for successful operation are provision for the lifting of the level of the plucking-table, as growth demands, and a careful timing of the harvesting operation. Strict uniformity of plucking rounds is not conducive to good results. Much intensive and creative effort will be needed before mechanical plucking becomes a normal routine operation.

REFERENCES

1. TUBBS, F. R., *Investigations on the Planting, Pruning and Plucking of the Tea Bush*, Tea Research Institute of Ceylon, Bulletin No. 15, 1936.
2. EDEN, T., *Emp. J. exp. Agric.*, 1944, **12**, 177.
3. ——, *Monographs on Tea Production in Ceylon*, No. 1, 25, 1949.
4. GADD, C. H., *Tea Quarterly*, 1928, **1**, 89.
5. TUBBS, F. R., *Journal of Pomology*, 1936, **14**, 317.
6. Tea Research Institute of East Africa, Annual Report, 1950, 7.
7. EDEN, T., *Tea Quarterly*, 1946, **18**, 55.
8. COOPER, H. R., *Indian Tea Association Quarterly Journal*, 1931–2, 120.
9. ——, *Indian Tea Association Quarterly Journal*, 1931–2, 179.
10. PORTSMOUTH, G. B., *Tea Quarterly*, 1953, **24**, 17.
11. VISSER, T., *Tea Quarterly*, 1960, **31**, 38.
12. HADFIELD, W., *Two and a Bud*, Indian Tea Association, 1963 (No. 4), 9.
13. Tocklai Experimental Station, Annual Report, 1959, 278.
14. WRIGHT, S. J. *Tea Quarterly*, 1953, **24**, 57.
15. FAY, B., *Tea Quarterly*, 1954, **25**, 3.
16. GOKHALE, N. G., Indian Tea Association Memorandum No. 25, 9.
17. TOLHURST, J. H., *Tea Quarterly*, 1964, **35**, 57.

Chapter VII

CULTIVATION AND WEEDS

*Ecological Considerations—Tilth—Type of Cultivation—
Time of Cultivation—Weed Ecology—Weed Killers—Effects
of Weed Control.*

THE discussion of soil cultivation in relation to tea as an economic crop demands not only the consideration of what is known at the moment about the scientific aspects of the subject, but a quasi-horticultural review of the ideas on the subject that have been held in the past. The basis of arable agriculture is, and has always been, the tilling of the soil. It has therefore been a conscious and planned interference with the course of nature.

ECOLOGICAL CONSIDERATIONS

The type of vegetation that grows on virgin undisturbed territory depends on many climatic and soil factors and their interaction one with another. In one region there is the sparse vegetation of the tundra, in another the vast areas of grassland, and in yet others the tropical rain-forest. The science of ecology describes how the typical associations of plants found in these localities have passed through various stages till eventually climax associations of great stability have emerged. These climax associations have an economy which is perfectly adjusted to the conditions of soil and climate obtaining at any given time. Arable agriculture breaks into these sequences of vegetation, destroys them and alters the economies that have been established. There is strictly speaking no *natural* way of indulging in arable agriculture. The natural vegetation of boulder clay with flints overlying chalk, in Hertfordshire for instance, is the hawthorn scrub of the village commons or the classic Broadbalk Wilderness at Rothamsted. Arable agriculture involves the growth of plants foreign to the natural environment, and their development at a rate exceeding that promoted by natural conditions so as to secure an economic return. That this interference with the course of Nature has often disastrous effects on the fertility of the land is common knowledge. By speeding up the destructive forces that operate on fertile soils, it

64

26. Tipping growth after pruning

27. Pruning the tea bush

28. Types of pruning

(A) 'Clean pruning'   (B) 'Rim-lung' pruning   (C) Cut-across pruning

is possible to undo the constructive work of centuries of natural processes. Without due safeguards the simple act of tilling the soil always tends towards destruction. It is an undoubted and very unfortunate fact that after decades, or even centuries, of agriculture in the tropics, the agriculturist is still unable to create a stable system of agriculture that will prevent the continuous diminution of soil fertility.

Some authorities maintain that only in the dry zones where irrigation waters constantly renew fertility from distant sources can such stability be expected. Others maintain that if forest lands are turned over to agriculture they should be used for crops of the forest type.

Tea is such a forest crop, but, as cultivated in plantations, only partially fulfils the desired conditions. Since only a portion of its vegetation contributes to crop it cannot be grown under essentially forest conditions because growth would be too slow. The early history of the tea industry in all zones of colonial expansion shows that initially the cultivation programmes put into force were as far away as it is possible to conceive from forest conditions. The notions held in those days owed most of their force to the example of annual arable agriculture in temperate climates.

TILTH

The essential basis of arable agriculture on an annual basis is the preparation of a good seed-bed. Without good germination and early growth an adequate crop cannot be expected. In one short season the plant has to develop from a tiny seed, maintain its growth and accumulate sufficient reserves to store a surplus in grain or root. Physical cultivation plays a large part in ensuring a good stand and a vigorous growth, and in eliminating competition from weeds.

Under the influence of a false analogy drawn from a different climate, pioneer planters energetically cultivated a perennial crop, even when well established, as assiduously as they would have done roots or cereals. In a climate which is more destructive of soil resources than the normal temperate one, and in some cases on steep land that would never be practicable for an annual crop, the result was soil erosion and a drain on fertility on an appalling scale. In justification it could always be urged that in so wet a climate the land must be aerated.

It is now known that these methods were unnecessarily wasteful. In the nursery, and in the early stages of growth in the field, certain refinements in tilth production are still necessary, as has been explained in previous chapters. In the light of the foregoing argument it should be possible to relate tea cultivation both to present conditions and past experience.

The tea plant needs a well-aerated soil but this is more satisfactorily provided by good drainage than by cultivation that is relatively shallow in comparison with the normal root range of the bush. Effective aeration is not a matter of creating large air-spaces by means of a cultivation implement, but of maintaining air exchange in the

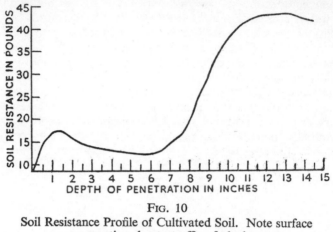

FIG. 10

Soil Resistance Profile of Cultivated Soil. Note surface
compaction due to traffic of pluckers

smallest pore-spaces associated with crumb structure. Air is dissolved in the rainwater that seeps through the soil. Provided that the percolation of this water is free, there is little cause to fear sub-normal conditions. Waterlogging, or even a moderate degree of impeded drainage, is inimical to good growth. The minute cavities left by decaying roots or other vegetation are the most effective means of securing the desired result. In so far as macro-cultivation is needed to incorporate this type of material in the soil, physical disturbance of the soil is beneficial. Soils whose structure is not moderately water-stable, and whose finer fractions wash down and form an impermeable barrier at the surface, obviously need cultivation to break this cap. But unless other measures are taken to improve the crumb structure, continued cultivation can only accentuate the already poor condition of the soil.

The sensitivity of the roots of tea to soils of high density has been mentioned previously. Pans, either occurring naturally or as a result of constant traffic of workers, and caked surface layers need to be dispersed by cultivation (Fig. 10). Experiments have shown that the reduction of a soil's tenacity by cultivation, whilst having only moderate effects on the spacial distribution of roots, has a marked effect on their volume. A well-cultivated soil frequently has one hundred per cent more feeding roots in a given soil volume than an uncultivated one.[1] The indications are that the qualitative aspects of cultivation are as important as its frequency.

No case for vigorous comminution of the soil can be made for tea, not only because a fine tilth is not required, but because in producing it a great deal of damage is done to the root system. Cultivation thrice annually in Ceylon produced a small but consistent diminution of crop when compared with annual forking. The average loss over a period of fifteen years was 3·3 per cent. This was certainly due to interference with root action.[2] Indian experience also substantiates this viewpoint according to Carpenter and Cooper.[3] Whereas in former times as many as six cultivation operations per annum were carried out, modern practice replaces them with a system of merely scraping or "cheeling" off weed growth. In Africa regular cultivation except as a method of controlling weeds is unheard of.

TYPE OF CULTIVATION

How and when to cultivate tea depends on the soils and climate in the various districts. The hoe that sliced off a section of the soil with its embedded roots has been condemned by the Indian experiments. Equally harmful is the "mamoty" fork or hoe "jembe" that is the normal instrument in Africa. Its introduction was a great disservice to the tea industry. All the cultivation that tea needs can be satisfactorily done with a gardener's straight fork, used to carry out what is termed envelope-forking. This amounts to no more than the insertion of the fork; the raising of the clod without complete detachment from the soil matrix; the levering forward and backward to form the envelope or pocket, and the leaving thereby of a ridge which acts as a barrier to soil-wash. Some tea soils are so pervious that they do not need even this mild disturbance.

If soils need cultivation to remove the adverse conditions previously described, then the accent should be on deep cultivation of a mild degree. The evidence in favour of this is twofold: first that it affects root-volume favourably, and second that it is a safer ante-erosion measure than shallow work. A soil loosened to only a shallow depth will easily become supersaturated with heavy rain, and the head of water so formed, lying over a region of relatively impeded drainage, will have power, even on moderate slopes, to start severe sheet erosion.

The cultivation of tea soils as a means of forming mulch designed to conserve soil moisture has had a certain vogue in the past. Its efficiency has been more evident in agricultural argument than in fact. The notion that the capillary channels of the soil were thereby broken, and that loss of water from lower depths was prevented, has not survived modern investigation by Keen and others.[4] It is not adequately realized in tea-planting communities that on many aspects of land the existence of a water-table plays little or no part in supplying the plant with water. The plant's reserves of moisture are generally stored in a layer of soil at what is called field-capacity, that is, in films adhering to the particle with very restricted movement except when rain is falling. A layer of field-capacity will frequently be sandwiched between two drier layers, the superior one created by direct desiccation of the top soil by sun and wind, the inferior one being the less moist because the rain was not ample enough to penetrate to it. The creation of layers of field-capacity moisture to an adequate depth is one of the valid arguments for moderate cultivation in that without it, on many soils, penetration of rainfall is slight and most of the precipitation is wasted as surface run-off.

TIME OF CULTIVATION

The timing of cultivation depends on the pattern of the seasons, on the nature of the soil itself and on the development of the bush during the pruning cycle. Some soils growing tea, notably in East Africa, are so unstable to the action of water that when recently wetted they puddle if trodden on or if disturbed by a cultivation implement. Such soils also easily dry out. To work them in a dry state is also harmful because by so doing the surface they expose to wind and sun is increased and their evaporative capacity is intensified. On all soils cultivation at the extremes of moisture content is to be avoided and difficulties arise because the range of moisture content that lies between the unfavourable states is very restricted. These African soils are derived from volcanic rocks, relatively new in a geological sense. The situation is less awkward on the old soils found in Ceylon. These are remarkably stable and, were it not so, the effects of erosion would be catastrophic.[5] Their cultivable range is also great and it is seldom that, provided rain is not actually falling, cultivation has to be delayed more than a day because of risk of damaging the soil structure.[6] Bearing these fundamental principles in mind, the decision as to when soil and weather conditions unite to give suitable or unsuitable conditions for cultivation can only be rationally made in the light of experience on the spot.

The third consideration, that of timing in relation to the growth of the bush, centres round the damage done to roots. As previously explained that depends in turn on the type of cultivation carried out, and on the kind of implement used. Generally speaking least damage is done by cultivation operations when they closely follow pruning, i.e. when the root system is dormant and before the new growth has made much progress. There is, however, one important reservation to be made. Just because the feeding root system has less demands made on it at this time, it is folly to suppose that violent cultivation operations can then be carried out with impunity. If the action is vigorous enough to break the lateral "extension" roots two deleterious effects are produced. First the area from which new feeding roots can develop is reduced; and second, the food reserves on which these roots depend for sustenance are likewise depleted, since these reserves are stored in the tissues of the larger roots.

Vigorous action against noxious and deep-rooted weeds in both India and Africa has caused identical effects, to wit, a die-back of branches due not only to interference with supplies of moisture, but to deficiency in starch reserves required for regeneration and expansion of the frame and foliage of the plant. In Ceylon where weed infestation is less prevalent owing, amongst other reasons, to less fertile soils, the milder form of cultivation that prevails there has never in the writer's experience been followed by such noticeably unwelcome effects.

WEED ECOLOGY

In every system of agriculture, after the formation of a seed-bed for the initial growth of the crop, the main purpose of cultivation is the control of weeds. The competition by weeds for soil moisture and nutrient needs little stressing in communities of agricultural workers, though when the losses are illustrated by figures they are capable of surprising even hardened agriculturists. Because the baneful effects are so pronounced, the possibility of growing tea on any system akin to forestry is unthinkable. In the wet tropics, which suit tea cultivation so well, the problem of weeds is specially severe. Their growth is so lush that they have created an impression that tropical soils are more fertile than is actually the case. Their ecology is such that, almost always, they have the advantage in proliferation over the crop in which they grow.

The ideal conditions on a tea estate would be to have no bare soil but a moderate growth of weeds as a check to soil erosion. It is noticeable that where weed growth in tea is most prolific, there is, with a well-defined exception to be mentioned later, less disposition

to overstate their inimical effects than where the problem of eradication is less difficult. The fact is that there are weeds *and* weeds.

In the hierarchy of weeds, the soft annual dicotyledons, despite the
fact that they transpire large quantities of soil moisture, are by
general consent, and on the evidence of experimental trials, the least
undesirable. Many are shallow-rooting and die back in dry weather
and their control is relatively easy. Perennials are naturally more
troublesome. Grasses of all kinds are pernicious, especially perennials with stolons which ramify in the soil; and from whose every
node the green blades emerge. Even the fibrous-rooted grasses are a
pest because, in common with other species, they are extremely avid
for nitrogen. In competition with a slow-growing plant of the nature
of tea they induce nitrogen starvation which is plainly visible in the
yellowing of tea foliage.

The stoloniferous species can easily create one of the most intract-
able problems for the tea-grower. Their roots are ubiquitous, and
contain ample supplies of food reserves if the grass is left to mature.
Any attempt at eradication by means of cultivation is bound to break
up the stolons into small pieces, each of which can develop into a
full-grown plant, and thus aggravate an already grievous situation.
In theory, after strenuous removal by digging, the dissected roots,
having diminished reserves to fall back upon, should be capable of
control by frequent cutting of the green leaves. If this can be done
so often that the subsequent growth is made at the expense of stored
reserves, before the leaves are numerous enough, or developed enough,
to replenish the stocks, the reserves are depleted and the plant must
die. This treatment can be shown to be effective on a small scale, but
in practice, the time, labour and money involved generally proves
prohibitive or impractical on a large scale.

WEED-KILLERS

Weeding ranks second in labour costs on the average estate.
Wright assessed the labour employed as one-fifth of the total needed
for field operations in Ceylon. In India and Africa the problem of
control is equally critical. New hopes for its solution centre on the use
of weed-killers. The Tea Research Institutes have been slow to respond
to this need. The best experimental guidance comes from Tocklai
whence four years' results have been published.[9]

There is a variety of preparations on the market and at present
those which seem to be most satisfactory are derivatives of (*a*)
2-chloro-4,6-bis(ethylamino)-s-triazine   and   (*b*) 2,2-dichloropro-
pionic acid. The former is of low solubility and is not readily transported from the scene of action. Absorbed by the roots it deranges

photosynthesis and is effective on dicotyledons and some shallow-rooting grasses. The latter chemical is specific for grasses and can be successfully used against such scourges as *Panicum repens*, *Imperata cylindrica* and African Couch *Digittaria scalarum*.

The Tocklai investigations show that the Simazine formulation of (*a*), at the rate of 12 lb. per acre in 80 gallons of water, was highly lethal to weeds in mature tea. At lower concentrations it was serviceable on seed and vegetative propagation beds. The proprionic acid (*b*) used as dalapon (=dowpon; basfapon), controlled 70 per cent of *Imperata* sp. when used in three divided doses of 4 lb. Dalapon is absorbed by the leaves and tea needs protection during application. Its use before rain or in prolonged dry weather is inefficient. Young, rapidly growing grass about three inches high is in the most susceptible stage. Trials in Kenya demonstrated its effectiveness on *Digittaria scalarum* in commercial fields. Simazine and dalapon used together gave a 99 per cent kill in the Tocklai trials. The duration of effectiveness of weed-killers depends upon circumstances. For Simazine at Tocklai the time was twenty weeks. Results at the Central African stations were expressed in terms of rainfall. Effectiveness persisted until ten inches had fallen.[10]

In none of the Tocklai trials did either of these weed-killers affect the yield of tea or the quality of manufactured tea from treated areas.

Present indications are that weed-killers will secure adequate control but not eradication. In Africa *Digittaria scalarum* gets its hold in newly opened land. Heavy doses before planting tea would be justifiable in these circumstances.

EFFECTS OF WEED CONTROL

To combat weeds a number of techniques have been devised and put into practice on tea plantations. The most direct is clean weeding either by hand or cultivation implement. In tropical regions this usually involves carrying the weeds off the land and burning them, because in these climates an uprooted weed can either re-establish itself in rainy weather, or ripen and disseminate its seed in dry intervals. Composting would be agriculturally desirable, but in practice the process never kills all weed seeds and makes little impression on couch grass stolons. The practice of clean weeding has much to answer for in accelerating soil erosion, and on occasions it has had the result of magnifying the problem. Weeds, like natural vegetation, grow in associations, the members of which practise in part a complementary, and, in part a competitive economy. Clean weeding because it is never completely effective favours those species that come to maturity in a short time, and also have a prodigious seed production and efficient means of dispersal. One example of this kind is a common weed in Ceylon: *Drymaria cordata*, which can complete the cycle from seedling to seed in a month to six weeks. It produces large numbers of small seeds, which adhere to animals, human or otherwise, and thus become widely dispersed. Other examples are weeds of the composite family with multiple flower heads whose seeds bear a parachute pappus. It is a matter of observation and experiment over several years that infrequently disturbed weed associations maintain an almost constant number of species, whereas once the association is broken up a rapidly growing well-adapted species will soon gain dominance. The previously quoted *Drymaria cordata* and also *Polygonum nepalense* are instructive examples of dominant covers produced in this way.[7]

It is not possible to give a formula for weed destruction that will suit all circumstances. Very little work has been done on the fundamentals of the weed problem, but that little suggests a number of tentative conclusions. It is quite possible to weed too often and better results would frequently be attained by less frequent operations more carefully timed. The indications are that times of cultivation can play a significant part in developing or inhibiting a weed flora. On an area devoted to an ecological weed study in Ceylon some of the weeds were species that had survived the breaking up of grassland, but many were adventitious. Over a period of four years it was a significant observation that on this land, which was adjacent to old-established tea, but was not clean weeded, neither of the aforementioned species gained a foothold.

Some weeds do not thrive on poor soils. Of these, members of the genus *Oxalis* are examples, although in East Africa *Oxalis latifolia* is spoken of as "poverty weed". It is a matter of relative terms. In Ceylon its disposition is apparently haphazard and some attempts to grow it as a soil erosion preventative have failed although it will grow in almost any garden so vigorously as to become a pest. In tea it is probably the least harmful of weeds. Indeed in Ceylon, which is very clean-weeding conscious, the evidence given before the Soil Erosion Committee which published its report in 1931 showed it to be very favourably regarded.[8] It dies down in drought and so does not compete for moisture, and because it springs from a bulb, it develops quickly during the thunderstorms that follow the dry weather, and provides protection at the time the soil most needs cover to prevent soil-wash.

There is definite evidence on the way weeds respond to applications of fertilizers. Research into this subject by Eden and Bond in Ceylon has recently been extended to India with corresponding findings of which the most striking is the vigorous response of weeds to phosphate.[7] Increases of two hundred and fifty per cent have been recorded. Detailed surveys have shown that the effect produced is due both to greater and more rapid growth, and to the establishment of greater numbers of seedlings. If weeds are allowed to form a carpet on the ground and are periodically removed they can carry away from the location a great deal of nutrient. Although phosphate stimulates the growth, the depletion of phosphate is not the most serious. The tissues of the plant contain higher concentrations of both potash and nitrogen than of phosphoric acid and it is on these nutrients that the largest drain falls. Since these are more expensive to replace than phosphate the dangers of over-manuring with the latter are worthy of emphasis.

REFERENCES

1. EDEN, T., *Emp. J. exp. Agric.*, 1940, **8**, 269.
2. ——, Tea Research Institute of Ceylon, Monograph No. 1, 1949, 31.
3. CARPENTER, P. H. and COOPER, H. R., *Indian Tea Association Quarterly Journal*, 1927, 133.
4. KEEN, B. A., *Endeavour*, 1942, **1**, 52.
5. EDEN, T., *J. Soil Sci.*, 1951, **2**, 43.
6. Tea Research Institute of Ceylon, Annual Report, 1928.
7. EDEN, T. and BOND, T. E. T., *Emp. J. exp. Agric.*, 1945, **13**, 141.
8. *Report of Soil Erosion Committee*, Sessional Paper No. 3, Government Printer, Colombo, Ceylon, 1931.
9. Tocklai Experimental Station, Annual Report, 1962, 40.
10. Tea Research Station, Malawi, Quarterly News Letter, 1962, No. 25.

Chapter VIII

MANURING

General Scope of Manuring—Nitrogenous Manuring—Phosphate Fertilizers—Potash Fertilizers—The Effect of One Manure on Another—Time of Application of Manures— Method of Application and Frequency of Fertilizer Treatment—The Constituents of Manures for Tea—Bulk Manures —Artificial Manures and Soil Fertility—Manuring in Relation to the Crop and Plant as a Whole.

IN the second chapter a general indication was given of the variety of soils upon which tea is grown commercially, but whether old or new, virgin or otherwise, the bulk of the world's tea is grown on land that is not of first-class quality judged by the standards of the highly developed agriculture in the temperate zone. This fact is borne out by the further observation that moderately productive tea is grown on land that produces but sparse crops of the type usual in annual husbandry.

When during the Second World War tea estates in Ceylon were required by food shortage and legislation to use their undeveloped land for producing subsistence crops, the mediocre agricultural quality of the land was strikingly revealed. The same comparison is valid to a modified extent over considerable areas of both India and Africa. It is indeed remarkable that economic crops of tea are garnered from soils which leave so much to be desired.

GENERAL SCOPE OF MANURING

Despite the very moderate quality of tea-producing land as a whole; despite also the exhausting system of monoculture under which tea grows, regular manuring of the tea crop is by no means a standard practice even in plantations organized on an industrial scale. Even where an integrated cultural scheme is in operation, manuring with a single nutrient, usually nitrogen, is a widespread practice. Judging from experience, supplemented by information from trade sources, it is substantially true to say that the nitrogenous fertilizers are the first to claim attention, followed in order of

74

importance in the general estimation by phosphoric acid and potash in descending order of merit.

This empirical classification has received considerable support from experimental work of a short-term character conducted in tea-growing countries. It is only recently that long-term experimental projects making use of accurate technical methods have placed in perspective the fundamental needs of the tea plant. On the one hand the prodigal dissipation of nitrogen in tropical climates is generally conceded. The low level of phosphoric acid is less clearly recognised. The felspar present in so many soils of lateritic or allied origin has delayed symptoms of potash exhaustion on the older and less fertile soils on which much of the crop is grown. On the other hand in terms of the crop's inevitable removal of nutrients from the soil the usually accepted order is changed. The tea flush normally contains 4 to 5 per cent of nitrogen, 1·5 to 2·5 per cent of potash and less than 1 per cent of phosphoric acid. When exhaustion has proceeded over a period of fifteen years it becomes apparent that the relative importance of the three major nutrients assumes a rather different aspect.

Because the soils of the Ceylon tea areas are amongst the oldest and least fertile, the pattern of nutrient requirements has been thrown into more emphatic relief there than elsewhere. The nutrient responses which will be subsequently quoted will not necessarily apply in other areas with the same certainty, but since the object of this book is to discuss the *principles* of tea cultivation, the illustrations that follow can claim to have a fundamental validity.

NITROGENOUS MANURING

Pruning and plucking provide a stimulus for new growth and keep the tea bush in a continuous state of vegetative development. Moreover the new tissues are rich in nitrogen. It is therefore only to be expected that tea should freely respond to nitrogenous manuring. Both experiment and practical experience confirm that this is so. Long-term experiments have shown that moderate doses of nitrogen (up to 80lb. per acre) give a yield response approximately proportional to the amount applied, with no indication that the law of diminishing returns is operative. [1]

The standard of cultural practices has much improved since these classical experiments were laid down, and the success that has attended these trials has led to larger and still larger applications of nitrogenous fertilizers. There is a need for well-designed and accurately executed experiments, maintained over a period of years, to examine the responses at the now prevalent higher doses. In Assam and Malawi such trials have been in existence for long enough to indicate that the responses to higher doses lie in that portion of the yield curve where the law of diminishing returns *is* operative, though lesser returns may well be profitable. [16] Fig. 11 shows the actual yields and the mathematically calculated curve which expresses the general trend. The Assam data show approximately linear responses up to 120 lb. N.: the Malawi data on the other hand display deviation after 80 lb. Considering the whole range of doses, the Assam response is slightly more than 900 lb. for the first 120 lb. of N.,

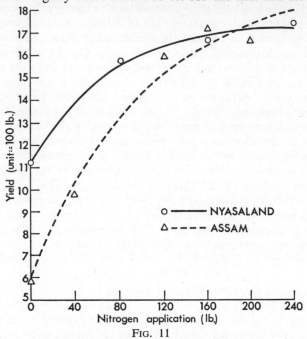

FIG. 11

Nitrogen response in tea, three-year average

but rather less than 300 lb. for the second 120 lb., whilst the Malawi responses to the two levels of nitrogen application are in round figures 500 lb. and 100 lb. respectively. A less detailed experiment in Assam assessing new growth (not crop alone) carried nitrogen applications up to 400 lb. A very steep decline in yield occurred after the 300 lb. level. The effect of diminishing returns at high fertilizer dosage and the implications as regards profitability need assessing specifically in all tea-growing regions.

The absolute efficiency of nitrogen in fostering increase in crop varies according to circumstance: a small bush uses its nutrient less productively than a large one. Experiments in diverse localities agree in placing the upper limit of efficiency somewhere in the region of six to eight pounds of crop (dry matter) for every pound of nitrogen supplied. (Carpenter,[2] Cooper,[3] Eden,[4] Jayaraman and de Jong.[5])

There is no evidence to suggest that the balance of nitrogen unused by the crop during a well-defined developmental period, such as the pruning cycle, maintains a recognizable residual value for future use. There is, however, a cumulative effect which must not be confused with residual value. This effect was assumed in a preceding paragraph where it was stated that a small bush uses its nutrient less efficiently than a large bush. The efficiency of nitrogen response on experimental areas where the manurial application was invariable from year to year increased 60 per cent over a period of twelve years.[4]

Superimposed on this gradual increase in efficiency are short period fluctuations associated with the stage of development of the plant in the pruning cycle. Early in the pruning cycle the response to fertilizer is small, but efficiency increases as the foliage and root system grow (Fig. 12). In a series of three-year pruning cycles the average yield increment for third-year applications was five times as great as that for first-year or pruning-mixture treatment. That this observation is inherent in the development of the bush is confirmed by the fact that it is paralleled by other nutrient responses. A significant and high correlation exists, for example, between the re-

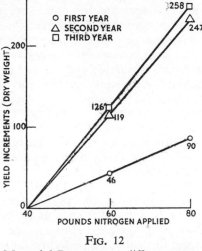

FIG. 12

Manurial Response at different stages of a three-year pruning-cycle

sponses to nitrogen and phosphoric acid over a period of fifteen years.[4]

The form in which the nitrogen manures are applied makes little difference except where substances are used whose nitrogen is low in concentration and of a complicated nature. Chief of these in moderate use are the low-grade oil-cakes, but materials like blood-meal and groundnut cake give similar responses to the so-called chemical fertilizer of the sulphate of ammonia, nitrate of ammonia and soda type.

The immediate response to organic nitrogenous fertilizers appears to depend on their rate of mineralization which, in turn, is related to their ratios of carbon and nitrogen content. As most of the organic fertilizers in commercial use have low C/N ratios (4–6) they are rapidly transformed and behave substantially like sulphate of ammonia.[8] The notion that these organic fertilizers become gradually available, and thus fit in with the progressive needs of the plant's economy, is not borne out by experiments; in fact the opposite appears to be the case, and the more easily the simple nitrogenous substances that the roots can assimilate are released, the better use the plant is able to make of them.

PHOSPHATE FERTILIZERS

The behaviour of the phosphate fertilizers is less uniform than that of nitrogen and responses vary greatly according to district and country. Nevertheless, although the phosphate content of tea tissues is low, and supplies are frequently sufficient, even in tropical soils whose low phosphate is widely recognized, phosphate response is by no means negligible and its use as a fertilizer for tea cannot be neglected with impunity. On older soils and on old-established tea, the phosphatic response is appreciable and economically productive. The fertilizer experiments of the Tea Research Institute of Ceylon, using applications of 30 lb. and 60 lb. P_2O_5 per acre showed no significant response beyond that of the lower dose: the larger application serving merely to move phosphate nutrition into the region of luxury consumption.[1]

The average response to phosphate is rather less than half that shown by nitrogen: like nitrogen the response is seen to best advantage as the interval from pruning lengthens. In fact, the consistent relationship between nitrogen and phosphatic responses without respect to total yield, period of the pruning cycle or weather, is one of the grounds for regarding the cumulative effects mentioned in the previous section as due to bush enlargement. The growth response of tea and other species grown in association with it (including a large variety of weeds), indicates that on soils whose reaction is favourable for tea, superphosphate is not superior to mineral phosphate as a fertilizer in regions of high rainfall.

POTASH FERTILIZERS

On a variety of tea soils and particularly on types rich in felspar, potash manuring does not show immediate results, despite the fact that there is a heavy removal of potash in the crop and in the pruning wood which is usually garnered by the agricultural labourers as fuel. This removal is certainly as high as 3·5 pounds per 100 lb. of garnered crop and may well exceed that in specific instances. The Experimental work in Ceylon showed that on a normal tea soil it required a twelve-year cessation of potash manuring before a crop decline was indicated on mature tea.[1] Thereafter, the appearance of starvation symptoms on control plots was rapid and spectacular. Moderate doses of potash gave responses which rivalled those associated with nitrogen, hitherto regarded as the crop producer *par excellence.* Marginal scorch of the kind typically associated with potash deficiency developed. Noticeable die-back also occurred and there was an alarming increase in total bush casualties. This high degree of deficiency developed within six years of the initial drop in crop yields. Research on the mechanism of these effects has still to be brought to fruition, but the symptoms are suggestive of a severe interference with carbohydrate economy of the whole plant.[9, 10]

The potash economy of tea appears to be more complicated than that of the other major nutrients, because side by side with these results are others which suggest that in the early stages of growth tea is more sensitive than when the plant is well established. In India where this effect was first noticed, the effect was evident on the total growth of the plant within the first year (Cooper and Woodford[6]). In Ceylon, this observation was not confirmed, but unmistakable responses to heavy doses (60 lb. K_2O per acre) were obtained in the tipping-growth stage when first the bushes were brought into bearing.[7] The further elucidation of these phenomena is very desirable. Young tea with a small extension root system has little storage accommodation for starch. Pruned tea when in a leafless condition is dependent entirely on stored reserves of elaborated material wherewith to renew its foliage. It would not be surprising if further investigation indicated that, in these peculiar circumstances, the potash problem was accentuated to a greater degree than in the period of maturity. There is also the distinct probability that the disparity in root volume between young and old tea is an operative factor: the scavenging power of the larger root system being able to maintain more easily the necessary supply in older tea. At present, however, these conclusions are speculative though reasonable.

THE EFFECT OF ONE MANURE ON ANOTHER

When a recognizable deficiency of a plant nutrient can be established by accurate experimentation it is a common experience to find that this deficiency reduces the efficiency of other nutrients. In scientific terms it is usual to speak of the limiting factor. By way of illustration, the literature of agricultural experiments contains numerous instances of null response to a given dose of nitrogen, but a marked response to the same dose in the presence of added or increased quantities of potash or phosphate.[8] A well-authenticated instance is known to the writer where a potato crop, receiving adequate doses of nitrogen and phosphate, but no potash, gave a lower yield than on land entirely unmanured.[11]

In formulating theories of manurial action we may start by considering how yield increments produced by two nutrients, used separately, compare with yield increments secured when both are used together. Experience shows that frequently the sum of the individual increments is less than the combined effect. In other words, the effects are not additive—the effect of nitrogen and phosphate together is more than the sum of the separate effects.

As regards tea, a clear case for this type of effect (described as an "interaction") has not so far emerged. Within the limits of accuracy of the experimental work so far concluded, even long-term trials fail to reveal a real interdependence between responses to several nutrients.

TYPICAL FERTILIZER RESPONSES
(Tea Research Institute of Ceylon)
lb. per acre: cycles of three years.

Response to	40 lb. N.*	40 lb. K_2O.	30 lb. P_2O_5
Cycle 1	+332	+6	No application
Cycle 2	+404	-20	+140
Cycle 3	+316	+40	+160
Cycle 4	+595	+117	+270
Cycle 5	+403	+225	+156

*In Cycles 1 and 2 the actual dosages were N_0 and N_{40}. Thereafter the applications were N_{80} and N_{40}.

TIME OF APPLICATION OF MANURES

It is a truism to say that manures should be applied at a time when the plant can make full use of them. This implies that regard should be paid to the stage, or stages, of development of the plant and to the seasonal characteristics of the region in which the crop is grown. Since tea is grown in diverse climates, and since the rate of development of the bush is variable, only the most general treatment of this subject can be given. There are a few obvious reservations to be made. Manuring at a time when the tempo of physiological processes, for one reason or another is of a low order, is uneconomic. Nitrogenous nutrients in the simple form in which they are imbibed by plants, are relatively easily removed beyond the range of root

29. *Albizzia* shade in tea (Assam)

30. Shade trees of *Grevillea robusta* and *Gliricidia sepium* (pollarded) in Ceylon

31. Young tea shaded by *Crotalaria* species

activity by drainage. Both phosphate and potash are in certain, not very well-defined, circumstances rendered relatively unavailable to plants. Being of a perennial habit tea is not so sensitive to times and seasons of manurial application as annual crops, but the cultural treatment of tea produces well-defined rhythms that have important effects. The synthesis of mineral nutrients into the elaborated compounds that nurture growth is carried out in the green parts of the plant, and the pruning operation regulates the amount of leaf tissue available for this purpose. Moreover, pruning affects the root system, the absorbing elements of which have largely to be renewed in each pruning cycle. Consequently the manuring of a leafless bush is bound to be inefficient. This statement sounds obvious, but it has required considerable experimental field evidence to establish the point in the minds of agriculturists; twenty years ago the so-called "pruning mixture" was an accepted fact, and to it was ascribed great virtue in promoting the recovery of bushes to full vigour of growth. The evidence which in due course changed prevailing practice has been given in the section devoted to nitrogenous manures, and in principle it applies to other nutrients too. Until the bush has passed the tipping stage, manurial responses are of a uniformly low order.

There is a dearth of direct evidence about how rapidly the tea bush absorbs the nutrients with which it is manured. The reasonable inference from long-term experiments is that as far as nitrogen is concerned the absorption is rapid. If this were not so it would be very difficult to account for the strict proportionality of response that has been described previously. When we consider the vagaries of weather, it would indeed be remarkable if, with widely different applications, the proportion of nitrogen absorbed by the plant remained constant no matter how severe or how slight were the risks of loss by drainage. It is more logical to assume that, as far as readily available nutrients are concerned, the supplies are absorbed in a relatively short time, and are stored for productive use when climatic conditions are favourable for growth. Such a hypothesis accounts for the observed facts that nitrogen efficiency, as indicated by growth and crop response, varies from season to season, but that, under any given conditions, the various increments of manure produce corresponding increments of crop. If this view is accepted it has an important bearing on the latest time in a pruning cycle at which a manurial application can produce an economic return. All the available evidence shows that after a pruning operation there is no residual value attached to nitrogen residues left unabsorbed in the soil. It therefore follows that a late application of nitrogen must make its contribution to crop before the cycle ends. Similarly, in regions where there is a wintering period when the bush is physiologically dormant, the same argument applies. Cooper and Harrison in Assam give experimental evidence that manuring later than July is less efficient in producing crop by mid-November (the end of the season) than when applied earlier, because three and a half months is not long enough for effective use.[12] If nitrogen is supplied shortly before pruning or dormancy, with insufficient time for absorption by the root system, the loss of efficiency is direct and obvious. If the circumstances are such that it is absorbed but not expended, then the loss is still experienced because at the time of pruning the stored nitrogen is removed in the prunings. The woody parts of these prunings are habitually removed as firewood. Even from the foliage-leaf little immediate benefit can be expected since their decomposition and release of available nitrogen occurs at a time when the plant is to a great extent (if not entirely) unable to take advantage of it. In brief, the beginning and end of a pruning cycle are equally unsatisfactory as occasions for application of a fertilizer as ephemeral as nitrogen. The use of a "pre-pruning mixture" to help the bush in its post-pruning development is condemned both by theory and practice.

The extent to which this generalization holds obviously depends on the severity of pruning and the amount of leaf left on the bush to maintain it during the redevelopment period.

METHOD OF APPLICATION

No experimental work on fertilizer placement has been done on the tea crop, and it is possible to argue only by analogy and observation. As practised on annual farm crops, restricted placement is beneficial in two sets of circumstances: (*a*) where fixation of the nutrient in a relatively unavailable form is brought about by contact with a large soil surface, and (*b*) where the roots of the plant are themselves very restricted in extent at the time of manuring. The first condition applies principally to phosphatic and potassic manures, and hardly at all to the nitrogenous kind; the second to annuals developing from seed. Although the absorbing roots of tea have to be renewed after pruning, the extension roots are already well distributed. It is a matter of common observation that the roots of tea grown at the customary spacing distances occupy the intervening soil mass very completely. Data on this subject have already been discussed. For mature tea, therefore, there is no satisfactory indication that restricted placement is superior to broadcasting. In young tea, a modification in favour of distribution near the plants is more logical.

The discussion of whether or not fertilizers should be incorporated into the soil by cultivation implements is fraught with difficulty because of the scanty knowledge of the changes that take place in the composition of the nutrients when in contact with the soil. The ultimate state of nitrogenous manures in the soil is that of nitrate, which is soluble and unabsorbed by any portion of the soil complex. Phosphate is readily fixed by soils of high iron content, and tea soils in the tropics are frequently soils of this type. The lack of immediate penetration of phosphate in a soluble form into soil is easily demonstrated by a laboratory experiment. On manurial experiments in Ceylon penetration below the depth of cultivation has been detected by Eden as has also its availability for plant growth processes several years after application.[13, 14] Alternate wetting and drying of soil brings about a corresponding, though chemically different, fixation of potash. On the basis of this meagre evidence, it is only possible to draw the tentative conclusion that it is advisable to distribute the fertilizers so that they are within reach of the absorbing roots of the plant to as great an extent as is possible, and at depths where soil moisture content does not fluctuate so widely as on the surface. All this notwithstanding, the results of cultivation experiments make it inadvisable to vitiate the effective absorption by over-vigorous disturbance of the feeding root system in the process.

The best compromise appears to be that in force in Ceylon where envelope-forking is the normal method of ensuring incorporation in the soil without undue root damage, and without encouraging loss of fertilizers and of soil by soil erosion. Furthermore, there seems to be no indisputable loss of efficiency when manures are spread in alternate rows only, a practice that allows traffic in the uncultivated row without hindrance to soil tilth and the culture of green manures in the newly forked land.

THE CONSTITUENTS OF MANURES FOR TEA

The actual materials used for manuring tea are generally determined more by availability and convenience than by any special suitability. Of those procurable it is usual to choose the less expensive in terms not of price per ton, but of price per unit. The accepted unit is one hundredth of a ton of the nutrient concerned, and its cost is easily evaluated by dividing the cost per ton of the crude fertilizer by the percentage composition for the nutrient under consideration. It is always advisable to add the freight charge to the f.o.r. price when comparing costs since long haulage can frequently change an apparently cheap fertilizer into an expensive one.

The chief nitrogenous manures in common use have formerly been sulphate of ammonia, dried blood, oil-cakes, fish and offals. Consequently the unit cost of nitrogen in sulphate of ammonia is usually very much less than in the others, thereby making this fertilizer the standby of nitrogenous manuring for tea. It is likely to maintain or increase its popularity because it can be produced synthetically from the air by an electric process and the electricity in turn can be provided by hydro-electric plants. The other fertilizers, waste products of processing industries, are likely to diminish in importance because the countries that produce them in bulk now tend to retain them to support their own subsistence agriculture rather than export them to tea-growing areas.

Urea has the advantage of high concentration of nitrogen and low transport cost, but is not suitable as the main source of nitrogen in regions affected by tea yellows and in need of sulphur. Neither urea nor ammonium nitrate, being hygroscopic, stores well in humid climates but ammonium sulphate nitrate is satisfactory in this respect and in Africa is the most commonly used of these newer fertilizers. Nitrate of soda tends to affect the soil reaction adversely if used over long periods.

The usual forms of phosphate fertilizers are superphosphate (more particularly in the concentrated form; phosphoric acid content *circa* 40–42 per cent), ground-mineral phosphate and bone-meal. Fish offals and bone-meal are likely to disappear from the market on the grounds previously mentioned.

The potash salts used are predominatingly muriate or sulphate. From the foregoing it can be seen that on the whole the more concentrated, and therefore less bulky, materials are generally used when these are available at favourable prices. Too highly concentrated fertilizers are not suitable because of the difficulty of hand-distribution of small poundages per acre.

There may be considerable changes in types of fertilizers used in tea cultivation. It is conceivable that synthetic nitrogen plants will be able to produce ammonium chloride more readily than ammonium sulphate. The effect of chlorine on plant growth is usually deleterious in areas of low rainfall, but has possibilities in regions with the high rainfall necessary for tea. Of other new products soda-phosphate is likely to prove of limited use because of its alkaline character.

Where a sound tradition of fertilizer practice, using all three major nutrients, is in operation it is advantageous to mix the manures, thus getting a bulk sufficient for even distribution. Some combinations of manures are incompatible and these, which are set out in every textbook of agricultural chemistry, must be avoided. Ease of distribution is greatly helped if a conditioner is used. Blood-meal, bone-meal or finely ground oil-cakes are all useful for this purpose as they prevent the mineral fertilizer particle from caking. A quantity equivalent to ten per cent of the total bulk is usually ample as a conditioner.

BULK MANURES

Cultivation in monoculture gives little scope for the use of bulk manures that play so important a part in rotational mixed farming. In the newer tea areas in Africa an attempt is being made to combine tea growing with arable and stock farming, but the endeavour is still in its early stages and it is too early to say what the outcome will be. Where bulk manuring is included in estate practice, the form of manure used is usually compost. There is no doubt that even if the acreage manured in this way is small, requiring a term of years to complete the operation over the whole cultivated acreage, the results will be beneficial. The principles involved will be dealt with more fully in the chapter on green manuring. Some of the effects of bulk manures are not strictly nutritional, and in this section only those that are will be discussed. The chief nutrient contributed by bulk manure is nitrogen, and of the total quantity contained in the average sample of farmyard manure or compost, no more than half is readily available. Experiments in Ceylon on young tea show that the combined effect of residual value, which truly exists in a bulk manure, and cumulative response, lasts over a considerable term of years. Fifteen tons per annum were used in each of four successive years on tea immediately prior to its being brought into bearing. Eleven years later, the effect was still not extinguished, and the average response throughout the period was little short of one hundred pounds of crop per acre.[7] The amount of nitrogen removed in the successive crops almost exactly balanced the amount of nitrogen applied. It is not to be supposed that all the nitrogen removed as crop originated in the bulk manure, but the fact remains that, over an extended period, comparable data for nutrient efficiency of nitrogen from artificial manures and bulk manures respectively reflects more favourably on the latter. It is becoming recognized that good conditions of soil structure, to which bulk manures contribute, influence the nutrient economy of plant and soil. That this is so is demonstrated by tea, as by other crops, by the fact that, in the presence of bulk manure, the responses to artificial fertilizers are improved.

The experiment in question gave interesting results not only for the tea crop but for the green manure shade trees with which it was associated. The vigour of the latter was noticeably improved.

Indeed on the area in question it had proved almost impossible to establish the shade tree *Erythrina lithosperma*. Renewals on occasions of pruning failed to establish a stand on control plots. Trees on these plots could make no headway against the ravage of a prevalent eelworm, *Meloidogyne* sp. When the compost (devoid of any animal residues) was applied, although eelworm attack was not noticeably diminished, the trees were able to outgrow the damage done to their roots by the parasite.

ARTIFICIAL MANURING AND SOIL FERTILITY

Much has been said and written on the impoverishment of the soil by artificial manuring, and most of it is the result of ignorance and confused thinking. The use of radioactive tracer elements in nutritional experiments has shown that the supply of added nutrients, by promoting growth early and vigorously, enables the plant to garner more of the ordinary soil nutrient supplies.[15] To that extent, therefore, the contention that artificial manures impoverish the soil is conceded. But this is by no means the whole story. In the first place, so long as only the nutrional aspect is considered, the same objection can be raised regarding any form of manuring. To put the matter into a proper perspective the whole economy of the crop must be considered, that is to say, what is added to the soil, what is taken away permanently as crop, and what crop residues are returned. As far as tea is concerned there is demonstrable evidence that artificial manures, properly used, by increasing the foliage residues of the bush, which are returned to the soil after pruning, can actually improve its nitrogen status within the range of cultivation.[3] Arguments from annual crop husbandry are of little point in these circumstances, because the greater part of the above ground growth is removed as crop, and frequently, as with grain, the nitrogen reserves of the harvestable portion draw on the vegetative organs during maturation and so concentrate the nitrogen storage. Only about half the foliage of the tea bush that is grown in the interval between one pruning operation and the next is taken away as crop, and it contains only about two-thirds of the nitrogen present in the leaves.[7] So much must be said in the interests of straight thinking. The viewpoint of this book is plainly that any system of monoculture is defective; that circumstances compel the tea planter to operate such a system; and that he must accordingly do what he can to mitigate those circumstances. In a sentence—artificial manuring can never be more than the simplest of the several operations that determine the plant-soil economy.

As a practical operation manuring is usually confined to the provision of the major nutrients nitrogen, phosphoric acid and potash. Where a monoculture has been cultivated for long periods the soil resources of accessory nutrients are likely to be adversely affected, though the deficiency is not so immediately recognized. The fact that the main nutrients are applied as compounds in which they are combined with other elements offers a partial safeguard for the supply of some of the other necessary elements. In addition, since phosphatic and potassic fertilizers are not pure salts they contain alien compounds as impurities. Thus, sulphate of ammonia supplies essential sulphur: phosphates are calcium compounds and also contain a number of trace elements. Potash salts are usually contaminated with varying quantities of sodium and magnesium. There is reason to believe that these adventitious supplements are not adequate over long periods of intensive cultivation; and to preserve the balance of soil fertility these accessory nutrients are likely to come more into prominence as constituents of manure mixtures. The specific needs in respect of sulphur, calcium and magnesium will be considered in subsequent chapters.

MANURING IN RELATION TO THE CROP AND THE PLANT AS A WHOLE

Cognate to the confusion of thought that exists about manuring and soil fertility is the fallacious argument that artificial manures force crop at the expense of the plant as a whole. Variations in the proportion of growth that appears as crop can be made by altering pruning and plucking methods, but if a standard type of bush management is maintained over a reasonably long period the evidence is absolutely conclusive that increased growth of crop is positively correlated with similar growth in foliage-leaf, frame and root system. Assertions that manures act as a stimulant forcing crop at the expense of the rest of the bush are totally incorrect in the light of the proven results of experiment.[4]

Whilst manurial experiments can put fertilizer practices onto a rational basis they cannot answer precisely such questions as how much fertilizer should be applied in a particular circumstance. There is bound to be a considerable element of empiricism in the application of experimental findings to commercial practice. Nevertheless there are guiding principles. The pruning cycle is the natural time unit on which to consider both yield and fertilizer policy. Although estimates of the amounts of nutrient removed or immobilized by the crop are not very accurate, it is common sense to replace the wastage, even if responses are modest or non-existent, and thus safeguard soil fertility. This is satisfactory as regards the more stable nutrients phosphate and potash. Nitrogen is in a different category. It is rapidly absorbed by the plant, and as rapidly lost if not so absorbed. Estimation on the basis of the known average response in relation to the crop level that is to be maintained, or if possible increased, offers a more logical approach. The use of short-period records of yield to determine replacement values has nothing to recommend it, more especially in regions of alternating wet and dry seasons. Such a rule-of-thumb method results in heavier manuring in advance of the period of less active growth and vice versa.

Another common fallacy is that it is possible to allocate nutrient supply in two distinct categories, that needed for maintenance of yield and that required for expansion, so that having enhanced yield by extra manuring to a preconceived and acceptable level, lesser applications will thenceforth maintain the new level of yield. This, as Gokhale[17] has shown, does not work in practice and is in conflict with the fundamental principle that a plant is an organism in meta-stable equilibrium with its total environment, and any significant change in that environment establishes a new equilibrium point, either higher or lower according to plan, unless there is an over-riding factor that renders the operation of other influences nugatory.

REFERENCES

1. EDEN, T., *Emp. J. exp. Agric.*, 1944, **12**, 177.
2. CARPENTER, P. H., ibid., 1938, **6**, 1.
3. COOPER, H. R., *Nitrogen Supply in Tea*, Indian Tea Association, Memorandum No. 6, 3rd edn., 1946.
4. EDEN, T., Report of 13th International Horticultural Conference, 1952, 1138, Roy. Hort. Soc., London.
5. JAYARAMAN, V. and DE JONG, P., *Tropical Agriculture*, 1955, **32**, 58.
6. COOPER, H. R. and WOODFORD, E. K., *Emp. J. exp. Agric.*, 1941, **9**, 12.
7. EDEN, T., Tea Research Institute of Ceylon, Monograph No. 1, 1949, 17.
8. ——, *Elements of Tropical Soil Science*, Macmillan, London, 1947.
9. PORTSMOUTH, G. B., *Tea Quarterly*, 1950, **21**, 18.
10. ——, ibid., 1953, **24**, 79.
11. Rothamsted Experimental Station, Annual Report, 1921–22, 98.
12. COOPER, H. R. and HARRISON, C. J., *Indian Tea Association Quarterly Journal*, 1930, 55.
13. Tea Research Institute of Ceylon, Annual Report, 1947, 26.
14. Ibid., 1948, 40.
15. BROADBENT, F. E. and NORMAN, A. G., *Proc. Soil Sci. Soc. Amer.*, 1946, **11**, 264.
16. EDEN, T., *Outlook on Agriculture*, 1959, **2**, 151.
17. GOKHALE, N. G., *Emp. J. exp. Agric.*, 1955, **23**, 96.

Chapter IX

SHADE AND GREEN MANURING

*Historical Development—The Ecological Effects of Shade—
Experimental Evidence—Short and Long Term Policies—
Green Manures.*

IN the plantations of India, Ceylon, Indonesia and Africa tea is
grown under a canopy of shade provided by interplanted trees of
various species. In its most systematized form this shade is best
observed in Assam where the interplanted grid of trees is uniform to a
very high degree. Elsewhere, owing largely to topographical difficulties, there is considerable variability in stand. Leguminous species
are favoured, but at high elevations their slow growth hinders their
rapid establishment and diminishes their usefulness. In these circumstances the non-leguminous species, *Grevillea robusta*, is widely
used.

Members of the genus *Albizzia* are the most frequently used shade
trees in Assam, the best known being *A. chinensis* (synonym *A.
stipulata*) and the more esteemed *A. odoratissima*. In Ceylon a larger
species, *A. moluccana*, was for many years planted as high shade but,
with the onset of blister blight of tea, has been discontinued. The
mode of silvicultural treatment of shade trees varies from place
to place. In Assam the unlopped trees provide a mulch of leaf fall.
In Ceylon and Indonesia, where *Erythrina lithosperma* and *Gliricidia sepium* are the more favoured species, lopping of the branches
for use as green manure is a normal method of treatment.

HISTORICAL DEVELOPMENT

The use of shade trees in tea plantations was originally conceived
as an imitation of natural conditions. A judicious blend of conjecture and observation of primitive cultivations of tea suggested
that the probable native habitat of tea was the albizzia forest of which
it formed one of the layers that are a feature of tropical forest. There
thus arose a prevailing opinion that tea was a "shade" plant.

In due course the presumed benefits of shade *qua* shade were supplemented by a recognition of the potential value of interplanted leguminous trees for the enrichment of the soil. Since a perennial crop does not allow of rotational practices, a mixed stand of tea and leguminous trees supplying organic matter and, presumably, symbiotic nitrogen, seemed a reasonable method to adopt for the preservation of soil fertility. For the past fifty years there has been a tacit assumption that the system of growing shade and tea together is advantageous because it stabilizes the long-term productivity of the tea plant. In support of this assumption it could be cogently demonstrated that, season by season, crop variation was rarely catastrophic despite great variability of environmental conditions.

With the advent of blister blight in South India and Ceylon in 1946 it soon became evident that shade so altered the microclimate in the vicinity of the tea bush as to intensify the incidence of the disease. Shade trees were accordingly substantially reduced in number, or even totally removed. In many instances this reduction was followed by a significant increase of crop. High levels of crop production have since been maintained with less shade or none at all, and a climate of opinion, unfavourable to the use of shade trees, has been building up without much critical consideration as to how much of the benefit observed may rightly be attributed to the removal of statutory control on crop production and the end of wartime rationing of fertilizers.

The Tea Research Institutes of Assam,[1] Ceylon[2] and East Africa[3] have all put on record their views on this controversial issue. The most able presentation of known fact and current opinion on the subject is that of Visser, carried out rather after the manner of a criminal trial by a "hanging" judge. Only in Assam, however, have any data extending over a reasonable period of years been accumulated. The Assam valley, with its large areas of flat land offering no difficulties of aspect to complicate the incidence of light and shade, is a specially favourable locality for experimental work on the shade problem, and is in sharp contrast to Ceylon, South India and a good deal of Africa.

THE ECOLOGICAL EFFECTS OF SHADE

The effect of tree shade on the undergrowth is obviously very complex and any attempt to isolate individual factors can never wholly succeed. Still less, without a great deal of fundamental research, can the interactions of those factors, for good or ill, be satisfactorily estimated. Nevertheless any examination of the shade problem must start with a consideration of the individual factors. For convenience these may be divided into two sets, one operating directly on the growing plant, the other working indirectly through the agency of the soil.

Direct	Indirect
Light	Soil moisture
Air movement	Organic matter
Temperature	Nutrient reserves
Humidity	Nutrient circulation
Physical damage	Root competition

Some of these factors are themselves interrelated and all are correlated with the physiological processes of the tea plant. A few examples will illustrate this point.

Photosynthesis is inhibited when light intensity is either too high or too low. When a leaf loses water too rapidly in relation to the uptake by the roots, the stomata close as a means of protection against desiccation. With the closure of stomata, photosynthesis stops for lack of diffusion of carbon dioxide into the leaf cells. Shade does undoubtedly maintain an equitable microclimate round the plant thereby reducing transpiration. To set against this is the added drain upon soil moisture resources by the shade trees. As far as the evidence goes this depletion is not overwhelmingly severe.

Pereira,[4] in Kenya, found that the presence of grevillea reduced water storage in a 15-ft. profile by only 1·5 per cent, and in the top 5 ft. by 3·5 per cent. The investigation was made at the height of the dry weather. In Assam, Barua reported a higher water content under shade of *Premna* and *Melia* during the dry weather than under tea alone. Venkataramani[5] in South India reports similar results with *Erythrina lithosperma*. In Malawi Laycock[6] found that the large forest-tree, *Albizzia gummifera*, made a heavier drain on water to the depth of 10 ft. than either *Gliricidia* or *Grevillea*. Age of tea and age of shade tree may be expected to affect the balance of water need and water use. Over and above quantitative estimates of conflicting factors a qualitative observation does occasionally illuminate a situation. The following instances are personally known to the writer. On an estate in Ceylon, abandoned for at least twenty years, it was the grevillea trees that succumbed to competition, not the tea. On another estate, during a severe drought every grevillea tree under ten years old died, leaving the tea relatively unscathed. The most striking shade effect ever seen by the writer was in the Tanganyika drought of late 1949 when passing through adjacent shaded and unshaded coffee-fields. The former were green and unwilted, the latter totally devoid of leaf.

How much symbiotic nitrogen leguminous shade trees fix is

largely a matter of speculation, though Wight[1] suggests a figure of 80 lb. per acre under Assam conditions. Most of the nutrients that are withdrawn from the soil by shade trees are returned and recirculated. As regards nitrogen shade trees of whatever type have an important part to play in conservation of fertility through the linkage of nitrogen with carbon in the carbon-nitrogen cycle.

To the question whether shade trees exploit greater volumes of soil than tea, thereby promoting a subsoiling effect, no generalized answer is possible. Several factors are involved: the species used; the nature of the soil profile; the age of the tree and the root morphology of both the tree and the associated tea. The writer has had opportunities of observing the root distribution of both tea and shade trees in areas stripped of both, before replanting in Assam, Ceylon, and East Africa. On some sites shade trees were deeper rooted than tea; on others the difference was negligible.

EXPERIMENTAL EVIDENCE

In an endeavour to interpret the effects of shade trees on tea as a matter of fact rather than of opinion account must first be taken of the work of Wight in Assam. His pioneer experiments covered a wider range of aspects, and extended over a longer period of time than those undertaken elsewhere. In his dissertation on "The Shade-Tree Tradition in Tea Gardens of Northern India" Wight[1] is careful to relate his findings to local conditions only. The experiments investigated the growth and yield of tea under both live and artificial shade. The former was provided by the Indian sau tree *Albizzia chinensis* and the latter by a canopy of interlaced bamboo slats which at noon intercepted 55 per cent of the incident sunlight.

Wight found that the artificial shade augmented the yield of mature tea by amounts ranging progressively from 57 to 84 per cent in comparison with unshaded tea during a period of six years. The live shade of *A. chinensis* also improved yields. In combination with applications of nitrogenous fertilizers this shade experiment produced a series of ascending yields in the following order of treatments. (1) Control: no shade, no nitrogen. (2) Nitrogen at the rate of 84 lb. per acre. (3) Albizzia shade. (4) Albizzia shade plus 84 lb. of nitrogen. In the presence of shade the nitrogen response was diminished. This shade-nitrogen interaction is broadly confirmed by similar but less extensive trials in Ceylon, Kenya, Malawi and Indonesia, all of which show either a greatly diminished response to nitrogen on shaded tea, or no response at all. On the other hand Wight's experiments gave an increased phosphate response under shade and he suggests that tea under shade has a pattern of nutrient metabolism different, from that of unshaded tea. In this view he concurs with Murray[7] who worked on cocoa in West Africa. Wight further suggests that *A. chinensis* has a role to play in the nutrition of tea that fertilizers do not provide.

The various agrotypes of tea described by Wight behave differently in respect of their reactions to shade and nitrogen respectively, and this would account for some of the variability in results from various trials. Moreover, since shade is patchy, some parts of an average field of tea are experiencing typical shade conditions whilst other parts are receiving full insolation. Hadfield[8] carries the matter a stage further by considering not only the shade effect of albizzias but of tea bushes themselves. Defining the desirable range of insolation as lying between the 50 and 80 per cent limits of full sunshine he counted the number of bushes that received this favourable intensity of sunlight at different times of day. Expressed as percentages of the whole population examined, Hadfield found that 8 per cent of the bushes were favourably circumstanced at 9.30 a.m. and that the proportion rose to 33 per cent by 2.30 p.m. As regards the self-shading of tea bushes he records that with close planting the lower regions of foliage may receive as little as 2 per cent of the full radiation. This, he remarks, would account for the observed fact that the good yields of early years, when the bush canopy is not continuous, are often followed by disappointingly low yields in the mature tea. Hadfield suggests that the different behaviour of agrotypes may be related to the leaf pattern, for example, the depth of foliage canopy and the angle of insertion of the shoots relative to the main branches. Both would affect light penetration.

The best-established generalization as regards fertilizers and shade is that of Wight and may be given in his own words. "There is a density of shade giving a certain increase in yield of the bush surface that cannot be bettered by using sulphate of ammonia under shade: but lesser shade would give lesser yield that could be increased by sulphate of ammonia. The biggest return per pound of ammonium sulphate, however, would be got by using large doses in full sun, but should fertilizer be discontinued yield would drop to a lower level than that obtained under shade alone."

SHORT- AND LONG-TERM POLICIES

The above quotation distinguishes between two different but related goals, namely the immediate achievement of high yields and the long-term conservation of soil fertility.

It is a truism to say that soil fertility depends upon maintaining adequate organic reserves in the soil. It is equally a truism to point out that the agencies that promote destruction of humus in the soil are more potent in the tropics than elsewhere. These facts have been given greatly heightened significance by the work of Pendleton and of Nye and Greenland[9] who have studied the beneficial effects of bush-fallows in systems of shifting or alternating cultivations.

Cunningham[10] has demonstrated the rapid deterioration of fertility on fallow land exposed to the sun. He used artificial shade similar to that in Wight's experiments and therefore there were no complicating "live" shade factors. The criteria employed to assess fertility were organic carbon (indicating organic matter), organic phosphorus and total nitrogen. The loss of organic matter with full exposure to sun was 2·3 times that under shade. For organic phosphorus the corresponding factor was 2·65, and for total nitrogen 2·45. These changes occurred in three years. In many tropical soils, including those types suitable for tea, the only source of available phosphorus is in all probability mineralized organic phosphorus. These reported losses therefore represent a drain on nitrogen and phosphorus that can only be diminished by shade or further accessions of organic matter. Shade trees thus perform a double function: their shade diminishes the speed of soil impoverishment and their leaf droppings mark a positive contribution towards recuperation.

In the absence of shade, the tea bush itself plays a part in safeguarding fertility by providing the significant amounts of organic material that are returned to the soil in the form of pruned leaf, or in some instances whole prunings. Figures for the weight of pruning leaf from both Ceylon[11] and East Africa[12] are in close agreement in showing that the amount is round about 80 per cent of the weight of flush removed during the pruning cycle. With such portions of the pruned wood as are not removed for firewood by the labour force the quantity might well be equal to that of crop. There is little doubt that the amounts of nutrient thus conserved are significant and that liberal manuring contributes to this maintenance of a capital stock of nitrogen by augmenting the quantity of pruned leaf returned to the soil. Whether tea prunings can fully stabilize soil fertility will largely depend upon the nature of the soil and the cultural practices employed.

GREEN MANURES

In regions where tea is cultivated under long pruning cycles there was in times past a period of a year or more after the pruning operation when the surface of the soil was devoid of cover. Leguminous bush species sown in this bare ground protected the soil from erosion and at the same time conserved the readily available nutrients in the surface soil which would otherwise have been lost in drainage. Eventually the development of the tea crowded out the green manure species which were then uprooted.

The success of this system of soil improvement depends on careful management. In contradistinction to shade trees, the bush crops, by reason of their density of stand, can be strongly competitive with the major crop. According to Cooper [13] the nutrient factor is the most important, but in Africa where tea is grown in areas of much smaller rainfall than in the Assam valley, competition for moisture is certainly a contributory factor.

The time of lopping is important because not only is a sizeable crop of loppings desirable but they must be sufficiently rich in nitrogen to ensure that their decomposition in the ground does not distrain on available nitrogen in the soil, to the detriment of the growing crop. These conditions are generally fulfilled if lopping is done just prior to flowering.

The contribution that green manures make towards maintaining a good soil structure is frequently overestimated. Martin [14] in Uganda found green manures were less potent as structure builders than grasses. There is no serious alternative to his view that the benefits of green manuring are associated with the regulatory mechanism of the carbon-nitrogen cycle which promotes the conservation of nitrogen.

Improved standards of cultivation have transformed the appearance and yield of tea to such an extent that a close canopy of tea is produced early in the pruning cycle and there is little room for interplanting. On new clearings the shade and wind protection that various species such as the Crotalarias and Tephrosias afford to immature tea that is not well established is still beneficial, if competition is carefully controlled, but the microclimate they produce favours blister blight infection.

In conclusion, though the nature of the shade problem has been more critically defined than heretofore, the question of whether on balance shade is desirable is still an open one.

REFERENCES

1. WIGHT, W., *The Shade-Tree Tradition in the Tea Gardens of Northern India*, Tocklai Expt. Sta. Report 1958, 75.
2. VISSER, T., *Tea Quarterly*, 1961, **32**, 69, 113.
3. CHILD, R., Tea Research Institute of E. Africa, Pamphlet No. 19, 24, 1960.
4. PEREIRA, H. C., Tea Research Institute of East Africa, Quarterly Circular, 1959, **2**, 4.

5. VENKATARAMANI, K. S., United Planters Assoc. of South India, Scientific Dept. (Tea Section), 1961, Bull. No. 20.
6. LAYCOCK, D. H., Dept. of Agriculture, Nyasaland, Tea Research Station, Report 1958–59, 7.
7. MURRAY, D. B., Reports on Cacao Research, 1952–54. Imp. Coll. Trop. Agriculture Trinidad.
8. HADFIELD, W., *Two and a Bud*, Tocklai Expt. Sta., 1963, **10** (No. 4), 9.
9. NYE, P. H., and GREENLAND, D. J., *The Soil under Shifting Cultivation*, 1959, Commonwealth Bureau of Soils Tech. Comm. No. 51.
10. CUNNINGHAM, R. K., *J. Soil Sci.*, 1963, **14**, 335.
11. EDEN, T., Tea Research Institute of Ceylon, Monographs on Tea Production in Ceylon, No. 1, 1949, 22.
12. GOODCHILD, N. A., Tea Research Institute of East Africa, Report 1959, 27.
13. COOPER, H. R., *Nitrogen Use in Tea*, Indian Tea Assoc. Memorandum No. 6, 3rd edn., 1946, 153.
14. MARTIN, W. S., *Emp. J. exp. Agric.*, 1944, **12**, 21.

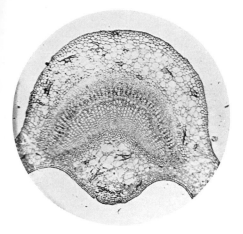

32. Phloem necrosis in leaf petiole

33. *Armillaria mellea* on *Grevillea*: bark stripped showing mat of mycelium

34. *Armillaria mellea*: fructification on *Grevillea robusta*

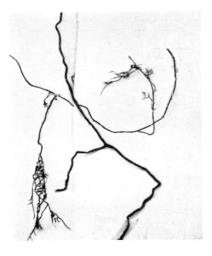

35. *Armillaria mellea*: Rhizomorph contrasted with tea root

37. Charcoal stump-rot (*Ustulina deusta*) showing mycelial fans

36. Brown root disease (*Fomes noxius*) showing typical cementation of soil

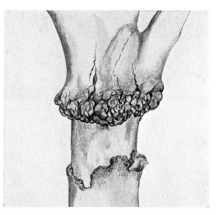

39. Ringing caused by *Rosellinia arcuata*

38. *Ustulina deusta*. Fructifications

Chapter X

DISEASES AND THEIR CONTROL

*Incidence of Disease—Physiological Diseases—Virus Disease
—Fungus Diseases: Root Diseases, Leaf Diseases, Stem
Diseases*

INCIDENCE OF DISEASE

THE monocultural conditions under which tea is grown commercially make the transmission of disease more difficult to control than where mixed or rotational crops are cultivated. The danger of disease is further aggravated by the fact that, in many tea districts, virtually no other form of cultivation is practised, and an epidemic outbreak of an easily transmitted disease can affect very large areas in a comparatively short time. The incidence of blister blight in Ceylon provides a striking illustration. Within three months of the original infection being diagnosed the fungus was reported from every district in the island. Length of time that the crop has been in cultivation has also a bearing on the spread of disease. A comparison between the recorded diseases in Assam, Ceylon and East Africa is instructive.

The Assam plantations are the oldest, but they are not so densely concentrated as in Ceylon, where it is possible to travel for a whole day without losing sight of tea. East African tea is no more than a generation old and the planting districts are considerably dispersed.[1]

The number of diseases reported from each of these countries differs widely and shows how age and dispersion of tea cultivation affects liability to infection. Hainsworth[2] lists thirty-five fungoid diseases in Assam; Petch and Bisby[3] record fifty-five in Ceylon. In contrast to these figures Hansford[4] in Uganda includes only seven species on tea in his survey of plant diseases found in the colony, whilst for Tanganyika the Wallaces[5] list extends to thirteen species. The activity of Tea Research Institutes in Assam and Ceylon has naturally tended to make the records more complete: since the establishment of a corresponding Institute in East Africa in 1949, Goodchild[6] has added to the East African list several species previously unrecorded on tea in Kenya.

The incidence of disease in tea may sometimes be distinctly localized for long periods. Ceylon and South India were free from blister

97

blight till 1946. The disease had been known in North-east India for about a hundred years, but distance from a source of infection and quarantine precautions had imposed an effective barrier. On the other hand, unknown and unpredictable differences in environment may lead to a disease or pest being closely confined although transmission is easy. In only one district in Ceylon is *Helopeltis* (Mosquito Bug) consistently encountered. In Assam shot-hole borer (*Xyleborus fornicatus*) is of negligible importance[2] though it is severe and almost ubiquitous in Ceylon. The most prominent of root diseases in Africa is *Armillaria mellea*, but it is a curiosity in Ceylon. Gadd[7] associates its incidence there with the introduction of *Albizzia lophantha* as a shade tree, but it rarely spreads to tea, and when this particular shade tree ceased to be cultivated no more was heard of *Armillaria*. Plants that are in poor condition are frequently made thereby more susceptible to attack by fungi and insects, and good cultural conditions are a help in inhibiting disease. Leach[8] states that the spread of *Armillaria* fungus is more rapid in dying or dead roots of tea than in living ones. But the principle that a healthy bush has more resistance to diseases and pests than a debilitated one cannot be elevated to the rank of a general and incontrovertible maxim. Shot-hole borer damage in Ceylon is much more severe on the well-tended estates than on adjacent smallholdings, where soil erosion and other undesirable conditions are unchecked.

The manifestations of a particular disease or pest may be widely different in different localities. *Helopeltis* again provides an illustration. In South India large-scale defoliation results from the attacks of this capsid bug but not branch canker. In Malawi, Leach and Smee[9] reported extensive branch canker caused by the insect, whilst in Tanganyika, Eden[10] has commented on the same symptoms which, curiously enough, are not accompanied by severe leaf-damage.

From the foregoing considerations it will be apparent that in a book of this nature, descriptions of pathological conditions in the tea plant can be of a general nature only, and no absolute order of importance with one exception, namely blister blight, can be laid down. For detailed descriptions of the whole range of pests and diseases the only adequate sources are the original papers, in which their nature and behaviour are described, or the monographs of Petch,[11] Hainsworth,[2] Tunstall[12, 13] and Gadd.[7] In this chapter the most prevalent in incidence and the most representative in type will be included. For convenience in classification they will be dealt with primarily in accordance with the kind of condition or organism responsible, and, as a secondary consideration, with the part or parts of the plant that they affect.

PHYSIOLOGICAL DISEASES

Bitten-off Disease

This is a pathological condition found in nursery seedlings and young plants derived from vegetative cuttings. It is not generally found at a later stage of growth, except when seed-at-stake is planted, because affected plants would be rejected before reaching the planting stage. The most noticeable symptom is the rotting of the tap-root (which in advanced stages may be complete), about half to one inch below the cotyledon level, with the result that the uprooted plant looks as if its tap-root had been bitten-off by a cutworm or other similar pest (Fig. 13). The aerial parts of the plant carry very distinctive symptoms. The leaves springing from the developing plumule are etiolated; they fail to reach maturity and drop off prematurely. Typical specimens of seedlings suffering from bitten-off symptoms frequently have no more than two banjhi leaves at the apex of the shoot. Internodal growth is stunted and, in the endeavour to survive, a large number of buds start to develop and then fail. The crowded leaf-scars give the stem a corrugated appearance. Eventually the whole plant dies. In nurseries that are afflicted by the disease, the stricken plants may be found in patches or a whole bed may be affected. Sometimes there is a perceptible gradient of symptoms passing from perfectly healthy to entirely dead plants. The type of distribution is very variable because the causes of the condition are twofold. The symptoms may equally be brought about by water-logging or by an unsuitable soil reaction. When waterlogging is the cause, the condition of the soil and the growth of moss or algae on the surface are useful indications,

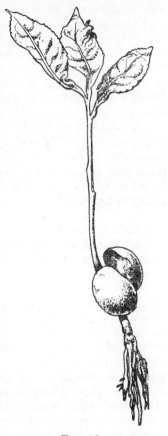

FIG. 13

A seedling suffering from 'Bitten-off' disease

but to decide indisputably whether unsuitable soil moisture or soil reaction is primarily responsible, pH or Comber tests are necessary. Gadd[14] has described in detail experiments on tea seedlings growing in media of varying pH and shown that the typical symptoms are reproducible and constant.

The most frequently encountered cause of adverse pH conditions in nurseries is the use of old building sites because they are generally already levelled and have a water supply laid on. The mortar and lime plaster from the walls become mixed with the soil with consequent alteration of pH values. Where sites have originally been occupied by labourer's quarters the wood-ash refuse from fires is instrumental in causing adverse conditions. Nearby gardens are always suspect for the same reason. In Africa where goats are kept in the homestead, the accumulation of decomposed animal excreta brings about equally unsuitable soil conditions on and around hut sites.

The soundest procedure when soils of adverse reaction are encountered is to select an alternative site. Where for other reasons it is desirable to retain an affected site, applications of sulphur will sometimes help to restore the soil to suitable reaction values. Child,[15] however, has demonstrated how recalcitrant old hut sites can be owing to long-continued contamination.

Tea Yellows Disease

The cause of this disease is sulphur deficiency. So far it is the only really important pathological condition in tea arising from a minor element deficiency. The causal nexus was first elucidated in Malawi by Storey and Leach.[16] Similarly deficient soils occur in Southern Tanganyika and Mozambique. It is probable that many soils in East and Central Africa have a low sulphur status. In this connection Beauchamp[17] has drawn attention to the low sulphur contents of East African inland waters. As far as tea is concerned, the disease is restricted to African districts and has never been reported from Asia.

The earliest symptom to develop is a mottling of the leaves. The network of veins remains green whilst the rest of the leaf gradually loses its chlorophyll and turns yellow. The leaf size diminishes, the internodes are shortened and a general stunting of vegetative growth is apparent. As the leaves reach a stage of severe chlorosis the edges tend to roll inwards, become necrotic and turn brown: the leaf tip is severely affected in the same manner. The leaves as a whole become brittle and easily broken and, as the symptoms develop, they drop off. Contemporaneous with this leaf shedding is a premature

I. Tea-plucking in Ceylon

II. A Ceylon tea-plucker

III. Tea-plucking in the Caucasus

breaking of lateral buds which, however, produce only stunted yellow leaves. The terminal bud dies and die-back of the shoot sets in. Not all branches are equally affected at first. Storey and Leach related this heterogeneity to the distribution of the roots which the various branches subtend. Eventually the whole bush dies. Histological examination shows that the development of the leaves and growing points is affected whilst they are still immature: affected leaves have fewer layers of palisade tissue than healthy ones.

The sulphur requirements of tea lie between those of trace elements, present at a level of a few parts per million, and those of the major nutrients. Eden[10] estimates the quantity required at 5 lb. for every 1,000 lb. of tea produced. When the deficiency is rectified by supplying sulphur the adverse symptoms rapidly disappear. It is thus a very simple matter to cure the disease before irreparable damage is done, and to prevent healthy tea from deteriorating on sulphur-deficient soils. The most practical and ubiquitous method of controlling the tea yellows disease is by using sulphate of ammonia. Since, in the course of normal artificial manuring operations, quantities of nitrogen between 40 lb. and 100 lb. are commonly used; since, also, sulphate of ammonia contains slightly more sulphur than nitrogen, the needs of tea are more than amply met in the course of routine manuring. Eden[10] reports an experiment on land which had, over a period of years, received 140 lb. of sulphur per acre. Three years after the cessation of applications there was no falling away of yield and no redevelopment of symptoms. In affected areas application of sulphate of ammonia must be made as soon as plants are put out into the field. Though very young plants do not respond, to a worthwhile degree, to manuring with the macro-nutrients, which are therefore not usually supplied at the time of planting, it is unwise in tea yellows areas to delay the application of sulphate of ammonia until the normal routine application is made later. A teaspoonful of ammonium sulphate per plant at planting time is in general an adequate safeguard.

VIRUS DISEASE

Phloem Necrosis

In the late 'thirties Gadd[18] reported a disease found extensively in up-country districts in Ceylon and tentatively ascribed the cause to an unknown virus. No organism could be isolated from diseased tissues and the distribution of the affected plants did not suggest a physiological deficiency disease. Following up Gadd's preliminary researches, Bond[19] established the virus nature of the disease by graft transmissions. No vector has been discovered. The search for a means of transmission is made difficult by the extreme slowness of the development of symptoms. Judging from grafts, a delay of two years may intervene between infection and manifestation of symptoms. The distribution of affected bushes is characteristic: diseased specimens occur in clumps of varying size usually quite small, but the scatter of these clumps is widespread. This seems to rule out the possibility of infection by the pruning knife. It has been suggested that an organism living within the soil might be a possible explanation, but no headway has been made in identifying even a probable species.

The diagnostic symptom of the disease is the necrosis of the phloem. When this is the result of virus infection it is always peripheral: there is occasionally a false necrosis found in the phloem nearer the cambium. Necrosis can be present in root, stem or leaf but is most constant in the root. The necrosis is not continuous and occurs only in small patches. Only fifty per cent of necrotic bushes show leaf symptoms according to Bond's surveys. Although less frequent, the leaf- and stem-symptoms are highly characteristic. In the leaf the necrotic midrib lignifies prematurely and ceases to grow: the rest of the leaf on the other hand maintains its adaxial growth. The result is a severe curvature of the leaf, convex at the upper surface. The shoots bearing the affected leaves and axillary shoots are confined to one plane, and the pattern of the internodes is characteristically zigzag. Roots on the other hand have no marked external symptoms.

Complete diagnosis requires an examination of the phloem tissues themselves, and, in advanced cases, a definite conclusion can be reached without microscopic examination. In roots the necrotic tissues can be exposed by carefully scraping the cortex till a dead brown patch is revealed. For stem examination it is best to peel the bark: when this is done the necrotic patches are seen on the underside of the peelings. Necrotic leaves can be diagnosed by nipping them off at the petiole. On examining the cross-section a brown arch of necrotic phloem is visible amidst the otherwise green tissue. The naked eye will frequently reveal this: at most a hand lens is necessary for confirmation.

Bond's survey of the disease brought to light a number of interesting features. In the first place, the disease did not manifest itself in Ceylon at elevations below about 4,000 ft.; above 5,000 ft. the incidence was severe. This suggested climatic masking. In the second place the symptoms of the disease were masked in the so-called high jats. Both these factors operated in the same direction, i.e. in confining the incidence of the disease to high elevation estates, since the great majority of these estates had been originally planted with low and susceptible jats. It was a noticeable feature of infected fields that infilled plants (which were consistently of a higher jat than the original hybrid-china) even though ten years old, and growing cheek by jowl with heavily necrotic bushes, were free from symptoms. Bond successfully separated the climatic masking effect from that of jat and succeeded in transmitting the disease by grafting through a symptomless carrier of high jat. The only form of control is that of severe and constant roguing, accompanied by supplying with symptomless carriers. The disease is a constant source of trouble and is spreading, and affects about 25 per cent of tea above the 6,000 ft. elevation. In the absence of a mutation that would affect the apparent immunity of the symptomless carrier, the localization and eventual suppression of the disease in symptomatic form should be possible.

In Assam, Hainsworth (loc. cit.) has reported a marginal necrosis of leaves associated with some necrosis of the veins. Whether this symptom is due to a virus is not known, but it does not appear to have the characteristic symptoms of the Ceylon disease.

FUNGUS DISEASES

ROOT DISEASES

Root diseases are of constant occurence wherever tea is grown on land previously occupied by primary or secondary forest because there are always some roots that remain after clearing operations. Root diseases disorganize the conducting tissues of roots and restrict supplies of nutrients and water. Until the depredations become critical there are no visible symptoms above ground. Eventually, a branch intimately associated with an affected root, or even a whole bush, suddenly dies. Petch considered that where a branch or a bush dies with its foliage intact the cause is almost invariably root disease.

Root diseases are particularly dangerous because their attacks are slow in development, and by the time a distinguishable symptom occurs not only is the bush doomed but one or more adjoining bushes may be seriously but invisibly infected. For this reason Gadd[20] stressed the importance of regularly searching for affected bushes by special gangs of workers, trained to recognize symptoms at an early stage. He further recommended that adjacent bushes should be removed, no matter what their appearance, as in the long run this involved less depletion of bushes than the usual *laisser-faire* procedure. It is very important that the search for diseased material should be thorough for experience shows that the primary source of infection is invariably a buried stump of a dead tree or tea bush.[21]

Shade trees complicate the problem of root disease control because when they have outgrown their usefulness they have to be felled. It is subsequent to this felling that major outbreaks of disease occur. Leach[22] working on *Armillaria mellea* noted that the fungus invaded those tissues which were rich in carbohydrates, principally starch. He proposed a method of treatment, before felling, that would reduce the concentration of starch in the roots. By ring-barking the tree to a depth that stopped short of the new wood the tissues conducting elaborated foodstuffs from the foliage were severed, but not those carrying water and soil nutrients. The tree died slowly because the metabolic activity of the tree exhausted the carbohydrate reserve in the roots till finally the whole physiological mechanism was deranged and death ensued. Without abundant carbohydrate *Armillaria* did not flourish and other fungi, saprophytic in habit, competed with the pathogen. Webster, Wiehe and Smee[23] report reductions in infection of tung trees from 10 per cent to 3 per cent when ring-barking is carried out. Gadd used the method with success for the control of other root diseases.

Ring-barking trees is an operation of some delicacy because if the surgery is either not deep enough or is too deep the desired objective is not attained. In the former event carbohydrate accumulation is not prevented: in the latter the tree dies with its root reserves intact. There have been devastating attacks of *Armillaria* due to careless ring-barking and impatience to get on with the felling.

A new approach to the problem is being made which both obviates the delicate operation of ringing and will speed up the whole method of control. In place of ringing a band of bark is merely frilled to help the absorption of the arboricide 2,4,5-trichlorophenoxy acetic acid (2.4.5T) which is prepared as a 2 per cent solution in light diesel oil and painted on the trunk. The 2.4.5T is carried upwards for the most part and causes rapid defoliation. The tree is, analogically speaking, turned into a deciduous tree. Carbohydrate accumulation ceases but metabolic activity goes on. As in the ring-barking technique, the vessels conducting elaborated foodstuffs are destroyed, in this instance by the band of arboricide paint. Callus and gum production is stimulated. In combination these post-treatment activities exhaust the starch reserves in the root. The technique of using arboricides is still in its experimental stage but results so far show that if successful it will reduce, by at least one-half, the time that must elapse between treatment and felling.

Reference has been made to the mutual antagonism of fungi in their attack on roots. *Trichoderma viride* is a saprophytic fungus which is common in soils with a plentiful supply of organic matter. It excretes a toxic principle which has been shown to inhibit

Armillaria mellea and *Fomes lignosus*. In connection with trials of D.D. (1,3-dichloropropene) for control of Poria in Ceylon it has been noted that the fumigation of the soil is followed by an increase of *T. viride*. This secondary activity may be an important factor in the control.[31, 32]

ROOT SPLITTING DISEASE

Armillaria mellea (Fr.) (Vahl)

Armillaria mellea is one of the most ubiquitous fungi and attacks forest and fruit trees in both temperate and tropical climates. In tea it is common in Africa and Indonesia but rare in Ceylon and India. The most characteristic symptom is the presence of longitudinal cracks in the bark at the collar of the affected bush or tree, caused by the destruction of the tissues of the medullary rays which radiate from the centre of the stem like the spokes of a wheel. When the bark or root cortex is lifted or shaved off a thick tangled mat of white mycelial tissue resembling felt is found overlying the wood. In long-affected specimens dark chocolate-coloured irregular strands like laces, which may be mistaken for roots, develop from the cortex. These are strands of fungal tissue known as rhizomorphs (= shaped like roots) and they are capable of extension to considerable distances, thus causing new infections in bushes, whose roots are not actually in contact. Leach[8] who worked out the life-history of the parasite in Malawi records no rhizomorphs on tea.

The first symptom of infection is usually the sudden browning and death of foliage characteristic of many root-disease infections. The wood eventually rots to a denatured wet pulp. Occasionally the fungus produces a honey-coloured fructification of the toadstool type, with characteristic gills.

The primary centre of infection from which the disease emanates is always an unexcavated jungle tree or shade-tree stump present before the planting of tea. The method of control is thorough up-rooting and burning *in situ* of the affected bush and the latent source of infection and, as has been indicated above, the elimination of surrounding (apparently healthy) bushes which though symptomless may nevertheless be already affected. By adopting this technique with stringency Leach considers that infections can be eliminated in twelve years. In new plantations infections usually appear after two or three years.

RED ROOT DISEASE

Poria hypolateritia (Berk.)

This disease is as serious in Ceylon, South India and Indonesia as *Armillaria* is in Africa, and is, if anything, more persistent.

Elsewhere its appearance is sporadic. In manner of development it resembles *Armillaria* inasmuch as it causes sudden deaths; is usually well established before above-ground symptoms are visible, and, in addition, produces rhizomorphs. Mycological examination reveals a fungal system that is quite distinct morphologically from *Armillaria* or any other root disease.

The mycelial strands proliferate on the surface of the root and are initially soft and white. At first they give the root a speckled appearance. Later they may form a complete smooth sheath, and later still they harden into ropes or plates of a distinct red colour. To reveal these symptoms the root needs careful washing or scraping. Occasionally fructifications are found at the collar. In form they are irregular thin flat plates pink or red in colour, and perforated with minute holes.

The fungus completely disintegrates the root tissues destroying all structural characteristics and leaving a formless wet pulp.

The control measures are identical with those for *Armillaria*.[18]

BROWN ROOT DISEASE

Fomes noxius (Murr.)

Petch (loc. cit.) describes this disease as the earliest known root disease of tea. It is common but does not spread rapidly. Infection is invariably by contact, and affected bushes appear singly and not in groups. Old unringed shade-tree stumps are the commonest sources of present-day infection. The most characteristic symptom of the infected root is the adherence of a sheath of earth and gravel round the entire root, which is not easy to remove by washing. The mycelium of the fungus performs the function of a cement, and soil and fungus are inextricably mixed. The fungal strands are brown and can best be examined under the bark. The wood is not usually badly decayed. The fructification is rarely found in the field. Complete eradication of the affected bush and burning are usually sufficient to arrest the spread of infection.

CHARCOAL STUMP ROT

Ustulina deusta (Fr.) (Petrak)

The disease is common in India, Ceylon and Indonesia and is sporadically found in Africa. It is sometimes more difficult to identify than other diseases because the characteristic symptoms are not superficial. There is no visible fungus mycelium, but if the bark is lifted the surface of the wood is covered with white fan-like patches of mycelium. The edges of dead wood caused by the parasite's invasion are discoloured by black lines. Such lines are found in wood killed by other root diseases but in the example of *Ustulina* the lines are duplicated as if drawn by a badly splayed thick pen-nib. As the disease advances the fructifications develop abundantly. They are irregularly ovoid in shape, thin and plate-like with more or less concentric furrows, which make them easily identifiable. When old they are charcoal black and brittle: hence the trivial name. The presence of abundant fructifications releasing spores provides a ready means of spreading the disease. The spores settle and germinate on cut shade-tree stumps and the fungus ramifies through the tissues and finally infects tea via the dead roots. Petch records an instance of direct infection on the collar-pruned surface of a tea stump.

The fundamental control of *Ustulina* consists of eliminating stumps of trees. Ring-barking prior to felling as in other instances has an inhibiting effect though it is not so uniformly successful as with *Poria* and *Armillaria*. Gadd[7] explains this by showing that the lignified tissues of the wood itself are sufficient to maintain fungal growth even though stored root reserves are depleted or absent. But ringing, causing death before infection, favours non-parasitic fungus attack after felling and puts the parasite at a disadvantage. Nevertheless, in addition to ringing, the stump should be cut off below ground level to prevent possible infection. Hainsworth (loc. cit.) takes the view that *Ustulina* can and does invade bushes that have died from other causes but this is contrary to the views of Petch and Gadd in Ceylon.

BLACK ROOT DISEASE

Rosellinia arcuata (Petch)

As a serious disease, *Rosellinia* is mainly restricted in commercial plantations to the one monsoon region of Ceylon and South India. Petch regarded it as of comparatively rare occurrence, but in its habitual environment it is not uncommon. The roots are covered with strands and sheets of mycelium which is more woolly than that of *Poria*, and turns through grey to black on maturity. Under the cortex the mycelium remains white and is grouped in star-shaped patches which are characteristic. So also is the shape of the hyphae when examined microscopically. The threads are divided by septa and at the point of division of some hyphae one end of the section is swollen giving the semblance of an Indian club.

The most important characteristic of the mycelium is its widespread proliferation through the surface layers of the soil, particularly when there is an accumulation of leaf debris and mould. Gadd[24] has measured the rapid rate of advance of a fungus through soil packed in glass tubing. The whole intervening space between lateral roots may be webbed with mycelium and the spread of the disease to adjacent bushes is thus easily effected. The fungus travels up the root to the collar, according to Petch, and in this locality produces pustules of conidiaphores whose conidia are disseminated by wind. The mechanism of transmission is therefore theoretically very efficient. In consequence Gadd regards it as surprising that the disease is not more widespread than it actually is. There is also a perithecial stage but this is not important in the field.

Control, in addition to the destruction, by burning, of affected bushes, centres round an adequate procedure for isolating surrounding bushes from the advance of the ubiquitous mycelium. Both Gadd and Petch recommend the digging of trenches which are to be kept scrupulously clear of organic matter. Petch also recommended the scorching of the infected bush by fire before removing it, in order to destroy spores, but Gadd regards this as practically ineffective.

The encircling of the collar of the bush by the fungus effectively rings the stem. The necrotic tissue sometimes dies and flakes off and a distinct accumulation of callus grows, in the manner usual in ring-barked trees, on the upper surface. Formerly liming was recommended as a specific against the disease but there is now general agreement that this is valueless and may, by promoting, locally, sub-acid conditions, be actually detrimental to the tea.

There are a considerable number of minor diseases of tea which in contradistinction to the above are not of great economic importance. Fuller details of these must be sought in the specified publications of Petch, Gadd, Tunstall, Hainsworth and Sarmah on diseases of tea. Two require brief mention here.

VIOLET ROOT ROT

Sphaerostilbe repens (B. and Br.)

In Assam this disease is described as widespread. The violet colour of the bark and the sickly sour odour of the tissues make the disease easily identifiable. The disease is associated with waterlogged soils which are not uncommon in the alluvial lands of the Brahmaputra valley and the peat bheel soils of the Surmah valley where water tables in the monsoon are high. There is no consensus of opinion as to whether this fungus is truly parasitic or whether the primary cause of death is waterlogging. Hainsworth (loc. cit.) accepts it as a parasite whilst Gadd[7] takes the contrary view.

Botryodiplodia theobromae Pat. is consistently found on roots of

IV. Potash deficiency symptoms: general debilitation, thin branches
and scanty foliage

. Shoot from potash deficient
ush, showing marginal scorch

VI. (1) Grey Blight (2) 'Cercosporella' disease *Calonectria theae* (3) Brown Blight (4) Red Rust (5) *Poria hypolateritia*

dead bushes, and particularly on debilitated bushes which have died during drought periods. At one time the deaths of bushes after pruning were ascribed to this fungus but the investigations of Gadd[25] and Tubbs[26] showed that these losses were due, as previously mentioned, to carbohydrate deficiency. No conclusive case has been made out for the parasitism of *Botryodiplodia* which appears either to invade already dead tissues or to gain entrance in the wake of other more virulent species.

LEAF DISEASES

Considering the large volume of leaf of all ages that is produced by the tea bush and the close cover of foliage that is maintained; in view also of the humid conditions associated with tea culture, it is a matter of surprise that the record of virulent leaf diseases during more than a hundred and twenty years of plantation tea-cultivation is not more serious than it is. Until blister blight migrated from regions with a wintering period and seasonal growth to those of continuous leaf growth, leaf diseases were not of great economic importance in tea-growing areas as a whole. With the exception of blister blight the commoner ones were caused by relatively weak parasites and their occurrence in a noticeable degree was associated with prior damage or debility which enabled the fungus to penetrate interior tissues. The importance of blister blight, both phytopathologically and commercially is now so great that it calls for more detailed treatment than the other fungus affections of tea.

BLISTER BLIGHT

Exobasidium vexans (Massee)

This disease, by far the most dangerous pathological affliction of the tea crop is now endemic throughout the tea-growing areas of Asia. So far it has not made its appearance in Africa. In the truly tropical areas of South-east Asia it has, in the past ten years, reached epidemic proportions.

First reported in 1868 as having been prevalent for ten years in Assam, it attracted little attention till the fungus responsible (which was described and named at Kew in 1898), moved in 1908 out of the Assam Valley and caused a severe attack in Darjeeling. Formosa and Japan reported it in 1912 and Indo-China in 1930. In 1946 it appeared almost contemporaneously in South India and Ceylon, since when it has also become a major problem in Sumatra (1949), Malaya (1950) and Java (1951).

How the fungus has been able to travel such long distances over both land and water remains an unsolved mystery, for the spores, though minute and easily wind-borne, are thin-walled and very susceptible to destruction by both high light intensity and desiccation. They are produced in such astronomic numbers that, once established, there is no hope of eradication of the disease by any practical means, even though it is known that the proportion of spores that germinate and gain access to the leaf tissues is an inconsiderable fraction of the number in the air.

The only reason why this disease has not completely crippled the tea industry, as *Hemileia vastatrix* crippled and finally destroyed coffee production in Ceylon in the last quarter of the nineteenth century, is that only the younger leaves are infectible; and consequently, with the improved knowledge of fungicidal techniques that is now available, the progressive debilitation of the plant can be adequately prevented, though at considerable cost in time and labour.

The symptoms are quite characteristic and follow a consistent sequence. The first is the formation of a circular or oval translucent spot which may be tinged pink, or may merely be of a lighter shade than the rest of the leaf. As the fungus proliferates, having gained entrance by the germination of a deposited spore and the penetration of cuticle and epidermis by a hyphal filament, the tissues it invades are deformed. The resulting spot becomes depressed, forming a blister, concave on the infected surface of the leaf which is usually the upper one, and convex on the reverse side. Eventually the convex surface becomes grey and finally white, the lower epidermis being ruptured by the pressure of a myriad spore bearing upright filaments forming a carpet-like pile. The ripe spores are ejected with some violence according to Gadd's[27] investigations and are disseminated by the lightest of air currents. There is no other type of spore additional to this hyaline, ovoid, thin-walled, one-celled basidiospore and no resting stage has ever been found.

Each characteristic blister is the result of one infection and the advance of the fungus in the tissues is limited; there is no ramification of mycelium through the entire leaf as may occur in brown blight infections. Blisters sometimes coalesce, but if the density of spore deposition is great, a large number of small blisters will result: sparse infections usually produce larger ones.

The fungus will attack foliage in the bud stage and in these circumstances the green shoot becomes entirely encircled and the shoot as a whole will die. After discharge of spores the blisters blacken and at this stage are infected by a variety of other leaf-rotting fungi.

Gadd[7] has shown that *Colletotrichum camelliae, Pestalotia theae* and *Calonectria theae* are all capable of this type of invasion. Their proliferation is not limited, and the consequent blackening and loss of entire leaves and shoots is a more potent cause of defoliation than the blister blight attack *per se*. A leaf more than a month old appears to be able to withstand infection. Certain bushes also appear to be less susceptible than others: the mechanism of this resistance is not known, and complete immunity has never been established for any particular strain.

The life-cycle from spore to spore is short. From infection to translucent spot the average period is nine days. A further nine days brings the blister to maturity, and spore discharge proceeds for about a week. At the end of three or four weeks therefore the cycle is complete, each blister releasing possibly a million spores. Given favourable conditions of climate, the build-up to epidemic proportions is rapid, as is also the rate of geographical spread. Cool, moist, relatively still air favours infection. Mist and shade are therefore conducive to the development of severe attacks. In dry periods and at lower geographical altitudes where temperatures and insolation are higher, the incidence is less.

The methods of control are three-fold, cultural, chemical and genetical. The latter is a long-term project. In choosing mother-bushes for vegetative propagation attention is paid to apparent resistance and less susceptible clones are being raised. For the day-to-day control of the disease the emphasis is now on the use of chemical sprays. Cultural methods were used with advantage until a coordinated spraying technique was devised. The object was to safeguard, after pruning, the development of leaf, which was liable to total destruction, by shifting pruning operations into a dry weather period of minimum infection. Lighter pruning was also adopted so that the period of recovery under susceptible conditions was shortened.

A toxic mist spray of cuprous oxide or copper oxychloride, at the rate of 4 to 6 oz. in 10 gallons of water applied at between 12 to 15 gallons per acre gives a high degree of control. These sprays are more controllable than dusting operations. Spraying should always follow plucking so that the natural weathering will reduce the copper in the next flush to less than the permitted 150 p.p.m. An efficient technique will leave no more than 90 p.p.m.

Forty or more spraying operations per annum are expensive. Visser[33] and his collaborators have correlated the germination of spores and incidence of blisters with sunshine records twenty days previously (the incubation period for mature blisters). The correlation was sufficiently distinct to suggest that spraying periods could be regulated according to weather conditions. Dry leaves are less prone to infection than damp ones and exposure to the sun for only one hour at a temperature of 85° F. is lethal. The formula recommended is that spraying can be suspended until the average daily hours of sunshine for the previous five days has dropped below 3¾ hours. Using this formula they halved the number of spraying operations with little loss of efficiency.

The varying susceptibility of different strains of tea has led to the establishment of relatively resistant vegetative clones in the affected regions. Though at present they contribute little to the practical control of the disease, they are being exclusively used for supplying vacancies, and for such moderate programmes of replanting as are in operation.

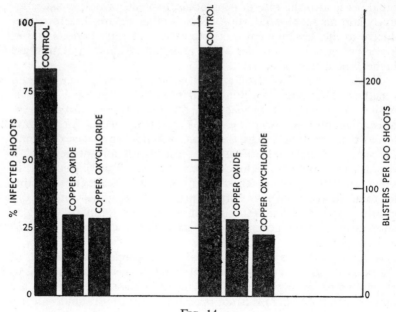

FIG. 14
Efficiency of control of Blister Blight by Copper Fungicides

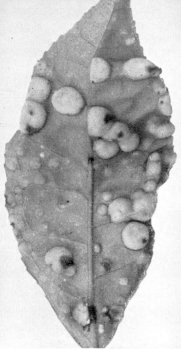

40. Tea bush showing blisters at beginning
of epidemic attack

41. Infected leaf with mature
blisters, some starting to
decompose

42. Control of blister blight
by spraying (S. India)

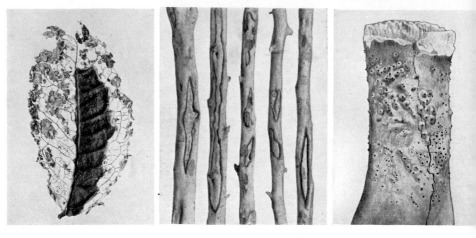

43. Effect of brown
    blight

44. Branch canker

45. Thorny stem-blight
    (*Aglaospora aculeata*)

46, 47. *Helopeltis* sp. and leaf damage

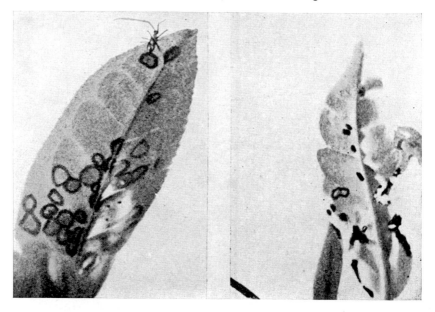

BROWN BLIGHT

Colletotrichum camelliae (Massee)

Brown blight is common to all tea districts. It is a weak parasite which is harmless unless it can gain entrance through a wound or into tissues that in some other way have been weakened. The mycelium is entirely internal and the affected cells turn brown and die: large sections of the leaf from the margin inward are destroyed and, in time, disintegrate. The spores are dark brown or blackish, formed in clusters under the epidermis which they rupture forming a small crater. These are easily discerned with a hand lens. Frequently an affected leaf has both *C. camelliae* and *Pestalotia theae* infections at the same time.

The two main agencies responsible for the leaf damage that predisposes foliage to the invasion of brown blight are sun scorch and hail. Blister blight and the punctures of capsid bugs are also prevalent causes of infection. Tunstall reports the infection of plucking points in Assam followed by severe die-back. In general there are no worthwhile control measures that can be taken against the disease which comes and goes as the cycles of wet and dry weather succeed each other.

GREY BLIGHT

Pestalotia theae (Sawada)

The general habits of this fungus are similar to the preceding. The leaves darken and dry up and the surface has a grey coloration. Portions of the lamina between the veins drop out leaving a skeleton of vascular tissue. As with *Colletotrichum*, previous damage to the leaf is a condition of entrance to the tissues.

BLACK ROT

(*Corticium invisum* (Petch,) and *C. theae* (Bernard))

Black rot due to either of the *Corticium* fungi is prevalent in India. In Ceylon the former had been absent for so long that Gadd reported in 1949 that it did not occur.[7] Loos[28] recorded the reappearance of *C. invisum* in 1950. *C. theae* is found in Indonesia. In India the rot is economically important. The leaves blacken, rot and fall off. They infect the healthy leaves on which they fall, and become attached to them by the mycelial threads that cover the under surface of the affected leaves. The spores appear on the lower surface as a powdery film. In the Indian winter-resting season the active mycelium of

C. invisum dies and resting sclerotia are produced on the stems of the plant and, surviving the winter, provide a ready means of new infection in the spring. *C. theae* has been known to produce sclerotia in culture but not in the field. *C. theae* produces ropes of mycelium which survive the winter and swell up and resume activity in spring.

The acute defoliation that black rot causes and the presence of a resting stage on the branches of the tea during winter make it a serious disease in India. Its control calls for pruning of the affected bushes and burning of the shoots so removed on the spot. This takes place in December, i.e. at the beginning of the wintering period. In spring the new growth is protected by spraying with a copper fungicide (0·25 per cent concentration) to which may be added an insecticide if ants are prevalent. Some new infection is bound to occur and Hainsworth[2] recommends stripping and burning of this newly diseased foliage. By plucking affected fields, in dry weather if possible, a potent source of infection from bush to bush is avoided.

"CERCOSPORELLA" DISEASE

Calonectria theae (Loos)

The fungus associated with this disease was long known as *Cercosporella theae* (Petch.)

The attack starts as a number of small spots about a millimetre wide which are grey with a blackish margin. On occasions the spread of the fungus is much more diffuse and may cover the greater part of the leaf after the manner of brown blight. The fungus mycelium is usually visible on examination with a hand lens on the underside of the diseased spot and this mycelium gives rise to the white conidial spores which are wind-borne. In severe infections the tea bushes are defoliated. The fungus also attacks a number of acacias that are grown as green manures and shade-trees in tea. These trees are the main source of infection as the acacia leaves fall on to the plucking-table of the tea bushes below. *Acacia decurrens* is one of the few leguminous shade trees that will grow freely at high elevations in a climate subject to heavy rainfall and constant mist. These conditions favour the disease. If the attacks are severe and recurrent, it is best to remove acacias in the affected areas. Generally, however, the disease has only minor importance.

STEM DISEASES

The woody frame of a long-established tea bush is seldom entirely free from stem diseases of one sort or another. The living cells of the bark offer considerable resistance to the invasion of some parasitic fungi but the continual pruning of the branches exposes woody tissues that are easily attacked by both parasitic and saprophytic species. Moreover on thick well-developed branches the vital portion is the continually renewed outer layer: the inner portion ceases to perform any physiological function and is composed of defunct cells. This dead wood is a ready source of food for wood-rotting fungi.

It is necessary therefore to distinguish between wood-rots that start in the dead snags of pruned branches and affect only dead tissues, though they may travel long distances in the core of the branch, and cankers that start from localities where live wood is killed by a parasite and are subsequently invaded by wood-rotting fungi. Both types can be observed in the average field of tea, but the former are the more frequent. Branches affected by either can put out new shoots from the undamaged peripheral layers, but eventually both types of infection lead to the death of the branch through breakage or ringing, with consequent loss of crop.

WOOD-ROT

When a branch is pruned the portion between the cut and the first new bud to develop lower down dies naturally for physiological reasons that have nothing to do with pathological organisms. No protecting callus growth can grow on these snags and they are subject to the aforementioned invasion by saprophytic, i.e. non-parasitic fungi. The fungi travel down the heart wood of the live portions of the branch and rot it internally. Quite commonly scavenging termites become active in the rotted tissue and their depredations may be mistaken for the cause of the trouble, but their effect is secondary. Some observers connect wood-rot on horizontal branches with sun-scorch that kills the outer bark layer and thus enables the fungi to penetrate into the wood below, but the validity of this explanation has been questioned by Gadd.[7]

The only measure of control is prevention. If snags are removed after the new branch has developed there is the possibility that callus growth from the surrounding live wood will cover the exposed cut surface and prevent subsequent infection. Painting of cuts with a purified bituminous paint, a resin compound or white lead affords some protection, but it not infrequently happens that the spores of the invading fungus have already found a germinating ground and wood-rot can proceed even under a surface completely covered by callus. Removal of partly-rotted branches involves the concomitant removal of such healthy secondary branches as still arise from it, and, in addition this procedure creates an even more extensive wound with accompanying die-back. In the long run, when an old bush has many branches affected, it is better to remove the whole bush and rely upon replacement rather than to tinker with surgery.

Macrophoma theicola (Petch)
(*Physalospora neglecta* (Petch), the perfect stage)

The origin of the true canker is quite distinct from that of wood-rot though at a later stage wood-rot may develop in addition. The responsible fungus is parasitic, and may be helped in its penetration by wounds or general debility of the bush. Sunscorch and weakening by drought are stated by Tunstall and Hainsworth to be predisposing causes.[13, 2] The symptoms develop in the rainy season when the spores of the fungus are extruded from the spherical fructifications sunk in the bark and set up new infections. The first signs of attack are dark sunken patches on the bark which rots away and becomes separated from the wood. When the bark is shaved the fructifications are sectioned and are revealed as white patches surrounded by a black ring. The active spread of the fungus is limited but lesions frequently overlap. In response to the damage the surrounding healthy tissues endeavour, by the growth of callus, to cover the wound and a ridge of new tissue forms round the sunken patch, but the process is never complete. Growth of the branch continues on the opposite side and the stem becomes deformed. The wood exposed by the canker is eventually attacked by wood-rotting fungi. The long narrow wounds edged with irregular ridges of callus are quite typical: in severe cases the whole branch may die back and, if the majority of branches are affected, the whole bush.

The control measures recommended are the removal of cankered branches, the use of a caustic wash on the frames and cultural measures such as mulching to protect the bushes from the debilitating effects of drought.

Aglaospora aculeata (Petch)

The trivial name adequately describes the superficial symptoms of this disease, the thorny projections on the stem being caused by the tops of the fructifications which crack and pierce the bark. They can frequently be felt, by running a finger down the bark, more easily than seen in the early stages.

The fungus is a weak parasite gaining entrance through wounds, mainly pruning cuts. Because it is a parasite it travels through and kills living tissues and may reach the main stem of the bush. The dead wood is uniformly brown in colour and brittle. In the early stages of the disease the symptoms are not easily distinguishable from wood-rot, because the characteristic thorns do not protrude till the branch or bush is dead. No system of pruning out branches is of avail in trying to control the disease. Gadd recommends the uprooting and burning of the whole bush.[7]

RED RUST

Cephaleuros parasiticus (Karst)

The trivial name for this disease is a misnomer. It has no connection with the uredineous fungi causing rusts on grain, apples, coffee and cotton. It is, in fact, caused, not by a fungus but by an alga, in which group sea- and pond-weeds also fall. The cell contents of the genus *Cephaleuros* are orange-red, hence the misapplication of the name rust.

This disease is widespread and important in India and is common in Ceylon. The alga attacks both leaves and stems and is more serious in the latter region. Dark raised patches, oval in shape, appear which turn red as the hair-like fructifications of the alga form a pile on the branches. The leaves drop and the stems die back giving the bush a thin and weakly appearance. In India the symptoms appear regularly on old wood after the winter-pruning operation when the bushes start to regenerate new wood and foliage.[29] Affected branches may fail to produce new shoots. The infection takes place before the pruning operation, about a year before the fructifications appear. Control must therefore be exercised at this time: measures confined to the later visible stage are abortive. Copper sprays are effective in controlling the disease. Red rust also attacks *Tephrosia* species grown as green manure and shade, and careful control or removal before spores are produced on infected material is a valuable and ancillary form of control.

Formerly the red rust fungus was described under two names, *Cephaleuros parasiticus*, a parasitic species, and *C. mycoidea*, an epiphyte living superficially on the surface of leaves and doing little harm unless the infestation was severe. No such specific distinction is now recognized. The one fungus behaves differently in differing circumstances.[30]

Poria hypobrunnea (Petch)

This fungus resembles *Poria hypolateritia* except that its fructification is a flat plate adhering to the surface on which it grows. It is at first pale yellow deepening to red and finally turning grey. Petch[11] lists it as a root disease. In Assam it affects branches to which it gains access through wounds, particularly pruning cuts. Careful pruning and removal of snags are the effective means of control.

Nectria species

Various types of *Nectria* cause severe die-back in India, but their classification and life-history has not yet been completely worked out.[2] In Ceylon they are of negligible importance. Isolated specimens have been recorded in East Africa.[6] Hainsworth regards them as wound parasites. The fungi are recognized by the pink spore pustules densely crowded on the stems. Superficially the disease can be mistaken for red rust. Die-back and a thin appearance in the bush are constant features of a severe attack. Any type of wound leaves the branch open to infection and hail marks are a common cause of attack. Cutting out of diseased branches, well below the dead portion, should be followed by spray protection of cut or damaged tissues by copper fungicides. Hainsworth records that attacks of *Nectria* and *Poria hypobrunnea* are frequently found in association.[2]

REFERENCES

1. EDEN, T., *World Crops*, 1954, 6.
2. HAINSWORTH, E., *Tea Pests and Diseases and Their Control*, Heffer, Cambridge, 1952.
3. PETCH, T. and BISBY, G. R., *The Fungi of Ceylon*, Peradeniya Manual, VI, Ceylon Government Press, 1950.
4. HANSFORD, C. G., *Host List of the Parasitic Fungi of Uganda*, *E. Afr. agric. J.* 1942–3, **8**, 248.
5. WALLACE, G. B. and M. M., *List of Plant Diseases of Economic Importance in Tanganyika*, Commonwealth Mycological Institute, Paper 26, 1949.
6. GOODCHILD, N. A., Tea Research Institute of East Africa, Annual Report, 1952, 24.
7. GADD, C. H., *The Commoner Diseases of Tea*, Tea Research Institute of Ceylon, Monographs on Tea Production in Ceylon, No. 2, 1949.
8. LEACH, R., *Proc. Roy. Soc. B.*, 1937, **121**.
9. LEACH, R. and SMEE, C., *Ann. appl. Biol.*, 1933, **20**, 691.
10. EDEN, T., Tea Research Institute of East Africa, Annual Report, 1953, 17.
11. PETCH, T., *Diseases of the Tea Bush*, Macmillan, London, 1923.
12. TUNSTALL, A. C., *Notes on Root Diseases*, Indian Tea Association, Memorandum No. 8, 1940.

13. TUNSTALL, A. C. and SARMAH, K. C., *Notes on Stem Diseases of Tea*, Indian Tea Association, Memorandum No. 16, 1947.
14. GADD, C. H., *Tea Quarterly*, 1940, **13**, 54.
15. CHILD, R., *The Selection of Soils Suitable for Tea*, Tea Research Institute of East Africa, Pamphlet No. 5, 1953.
16. STOREY, H. H. and LEACH, R., *Ann. appl. Biol.*, 1933, **20**, 23.
17. BEAUCHAMP, R. S. A., *Nature*, 1953, **171**, 769.
18. GADD, C. H., *Tea Quarterly*, 1939, **12**.
19. BOND, T. E. T., *Ann. appl. Biol.*, 1944, **31**, 40, 300.
20. GADD, C. H., *Tea Quarterly*, 1937, **10**, 36.
21. EDEN, T., *The Control of Armillaria Root Disease in Tea*, Tea Research Institute of East Africa, Pamphlet No. 3, 1952.
22. LEACH, R., *Trans. Brit. mycol. Soc.*, 1939, **23**, 4.
23. WEBSTER, C. C., WIEHE, P. O. and SMEE, C., *The Cultivation of the Tung Oil Tree in Nyasaland*, Government Printer, Zomba, 1950.
24. GADD, C. H., *Tea Quarterly*, 1929, **2**, 17.
25. ——, *Tea Quarterly*, 1928, **1**, 89.
26. TUBBS, F. R., *J. Pomol.*, 1936, **14**, 317.
27. GADD, C. H. and LOOS, C. A., *Trans. Brit. mycol. Soc.*, 1948, **31**, 229.
28. LOOS, C. A., Tea Research Institute of Ceylon, Annual Report, 1950, 44.
29. TUNSTALL, A. C., *Red Rust*, Indian Tea Association, Memorandum No. 14, 1942.
30. SARMAH, K. C., *The Diseases of Tea and Associated Crops in N.E. India*. Indian Tea Association, Memorandum No. 26, 1960.
31. MULDER, D., *Tea Quarterly*, 1961, **32**, 140.
32. Tea Research Institute of Ceylon, Report, 1960, 76.
33. VISSER, T., SHANMUGANATHAN, N., and SABANAYAGAM, J. V., *Ann. appl. Biol.*, 1961, **49**, 306.

Chapter XI

INSECT AND OTHER PESTS

*Control Measures suitable for Tea—Leaf-destroying Pests—
Stem Borers—Termites—Eelworms—Eelworm Control.*

CONTROL MEASURES SUITABLE FOR TEA

IN seeking to control the ravages of insect pests there are several means at the disposal of the agriculturist. First there are methods which seek to deprive the pest of an adequate food supply: they may be classified under three heads. (1) The raising of unpalatable varieties, (2) the production of toxic tissues by means of systemic insecticides, and (3) cultural means aimed at providing that susceptible stages of growth do not coincide with the marked prevalence of the pest. Of these three methods only the last is practicable for tea.

The second line of attack is to kill efficiently the insect or other pest in sufficient numbers to prevent proliferation to epidemic proportions. For this purpose biological control, by parasite or predator, and insecticidal applications have been successfully developed for use against tea pests. There are, however, severe limitations to the use of poisonous sprays or dusts, or, when sufficiently developed, to systemic insecticides in a crop such as tea where the necessity arises to apply chemicals to the leaves which are the portion harvested as crop. Apart from the risk of medical complications there are the risks of taints caused by sulphur or the newer insecticides based on dichloro-diphenyl trichlorethane or benzene hexachloride. These taints persist through the manufacturing stage of the leaf and render the finished tea unsaleable. Hainsworth[1] avers that, when used in correct concentrations, insecticides can be used without endangering the quality or flavour of the tea, but the difficulty arises of ensuring that the necessary limits are observed. The distribution of insecticides is not always under the control of the estate authorities. In East Africa distribution of DDT by aeroplanes in an anti-locust campaign so contaminated growing tea that a whole month's crop was lost.[2]

A further danger in the indiscriminate use of insecticides is that of killing useful parasites. It is reported from Ceylon that spraying against *Helopeltis* was followed by an increase in the incidence of tea tortrix and this may well have been due to the lethal effect on the *Macrocentrus* parasite of the tortrix larvae.

The use of insecticides for control of tea pests must therefore be approached with care, and must be done with due regard to times of harvesting the leaf. It may well be necessary to interrupt normal plucking operations so that, when eventually they are resumed, the new flush has predominatingly been produced subsequently to the insecticidal operations.

Such being the circumstances, there is everything to be said for combating insect pests of tea, whenever possible, either by cultural means or by biological control of the insects, without resorting to large-scale applications of insecticides.

LEAF-DESTROYING PESTS

Damage to the foliage of tea, with consequent loss of crop, or in severe instances debilitation of the bush, is of two kinds, that caused by leaf-eating caterpillars or by sucking insects. The tortrix caterpillar and the nettle-grub are the chief leaf-eaters: capsid bugs, mites, jassids and aphis are the prevailing leaf-suckers.

THE TEA TORTRIX

Homona coffearia (Nietn.)

This pest is known in Ceylon, India and Indonesia, but has developed seriously only in Ceylon. In India, the annual pruning provides an effective means of cultural control and in Indonesia it is inhibited by an indigenous parasite.

The moth lays its eggs on the leaf in clusters about a quarter of an inch in diameter which are oval or nearly circular and may contain a hundred or more eggs. The egg masses look like waxy spots. These eggs give rise on hatching to pale-green caterpillars which at full growth are half to three quarters of an inch long and are very active. They spin silken threads which they attach to the leaf lamina on each side of their bodies. On drying, these threads contract, drawing the leaf edges together, thus forming a protective pocket where the caterpillars live and feed. The caterpillars move from place to place webbing leaves together, and finally pupate for about a fortnight. The emergent moth mates and lays eggs for a new generation, thus starting a new life-cycle which averages two and a half months in duration.[3]

In certain districts of Ceylon the incidence of the pest was so severe that it was declared a scheduled pest. Collection and enumeration of egg-masses was made compulsory at weekly intervals, this period being slightly less than the incubation period of the egg (eight to ten days). The severity of attacks corresponded with the peaks in the life-cycle. There were five or six annually with a maximum in January gradually declining till August and building up again towards the end of the year. Severe attacks spoiled the harvestable flush for manufacture.

Attempts to control the pest by means of an egg parasite *Trichogramma* sp. were unsuccessful, but effective control was achieved with the larval parasite *Macrocentrus homonae* (Nixon), the Ichneumon wasp imported from Java which naturally controls the pest in Indonesia.[4]

The female *Macrocentrus* has a long ovipositor which is capable of penetrating into the leafy nest the tortrix has made. She is sensitive to the odour of the frass excreted by the tortrix and seeks out her prey. She stabs viciously at the body of the caterpillar, flexing her ovipositor and laying eggs, one at each puncture, in the soft tissues. The larvae that hatch feed on the body juices of the caterpillar which continues to live and feed. When the larvae eventually emerge they spin a cocoon which envelops the caterpillar and thus encompasses its death.

The control of the tortrix by the parasite is thoroughly effective for two reasons. Whereas the life-cycle of the host is approximately ten weeks, that of the parasite is seven, and there is ample time for it to enter and kill the caterpillar before the latter can produce a new generation. Furthermore Gadd[5] has shown that the *Macrocentrus* egg is polyembryonic and may give rise to as many as thirty larvae. The degree of parasitism is high, but not so absolute as to bring about self-extermination of the wasp from lack of a host. As far as is known *Macrocentrus* has no other host in Ceylon. From time to time minor peaks of tortrix incidence are reported, but they never attain a real degree of severity because increase in tortrix is quickly outrun by the parasite. As a result of this successful biological control the tortrix has been removed from the list of scheduled pests.

NETTLE GRUBS

Eleven species of nettle grub are recorded as being associated with tea. They belong to seven genera, viz. *Thosea*, *Macroplectra*, *Parasa*, *Scopelodes*, *Spatulifimbria*, *Narosa* and *Belippa*.[6]

They are the larvae of nocturnal moths, are oval in shape and, having either no legs or only rudimentary ones, move slowly in the manner of slugs. They live and feed on the underside of mature leaves. They pupate in the form of a hard spherical cocoon which in the case of *Thosea cervina* (Moore) has a remarkable resemblance to a tea seed. The grubs themselves are varied in colour, mostly bright green or orange with distinctive markings. *Spatulifimbria castaneiceps* Hmp. has red bands; *Parasa lepida* (Cram) is blue striped. The genus *Thosea* has four species found on tea; the other genera one only. The damage they cause is generally not great, though at times a considerable degree of defoliation can occur. Their importance as a pest is due to the tufts of branching stinging spines on their backs which can inflict a painful wound when touched. A severe attack of nettle grub makes a field of tea virtually unpluckable on this account. They also soil the flush with their faeces.

The control of nettle grub seldom calls for applications of insecticides. They are controlled to a certain extent in the larval stages by brachonid and eulophid parasites.[7, 8] At the stage when the grubs of *Macroplectra nararia* become mature they are usually killed in large quantities by a wilt disease due to a granulosis virus.[9] *Thosea* is unaffected.[10]

In Ceylon where serious outbreaks occur periodically, the pest is associated with those districts that have only the North-east Monsoon rains, but its incidence is not confined to the dry weather. In India *Thosea* species are the most prevalent: in Ceylon *Macroplectra nararia* Moore has the widest range.[7]

TEA MOSQUITO BUG

Helopeltis sp.

Helopeltis bears no relationship to the mosquito and its trivial name is an unfortunate misnomer. A certain similarity in size and posture is the only resemblance. The mature insect has four wings (the mosquito has two only) and a characteristic knobbed dorsal spine. It is a true capsid bug and sucks the juices from the plant tissues by inserting its proboscis into young leaves and stems. The eggs are embedded in the buds and axils of the leaves and are sausage-shaped with two protruding and unequal hairs. The eggs give rise to nymphs which are at first wingless and which pass through five moults before becoming completely mature. The size and colour of the perfect insect varies according to the species. In India and Ceylon the common species is *Helopeltis theivora* Wth., and there is some doubt whether the previously recorded *H. antonii* Sign. is not a misnomer for *H. theivora*. This species is orange-coloured across

the shoulders in the female: the male in maturity is almost black.[11]
In Africa a larger more brightly coloured species is prevalent:
H. bergrothi Reut., the body of which is bright scarlet.[12]

Helopeltis is a rather elusive pest as it is nocturnal in habit and
moves and feeds only at night or early in the morning. During most
of the day it secretes itself in the depths of the bush on the underside of
the leaves. It likes a moist warm atmosphere and the microclimate
of the bush provides this. It is generally more prevalent in tea that
has a cover of shade trees.

The nature and extent of the damage done by *Helopeltis* varies
with the species. In India and Ceylon the typical attack is on the
young leaves. The proboscis punctures the leaf frequently in many
places and, besides withdrawing the plant juices, injects its saliva
into the tissues. This saliva kills the injected cells and a translucent
spot quickly turning brown is formed. The tissues die and the dead
portions drop out leaving a hole one to two millimetres in diameter.
In addition the growth of the leaf in the neighbourhood of the puncture is inhibited and the leaf becomes noticeably dry and crinkled.
In severe attacks the final state may be one of considerable defoliation.

In Africa leaf punctures are also found, but they do not occur with
such frequency as in India and Ceylon. Judged from the appearance
of the leaf the pest would be regarded as a minor one except on young
plants in the nursery or post-nursery stage. *H. bergrothi*, however,
does not confine its attacks to leaves or young petioles, but traverses
considerable lengths of green stem, in some instances making punctures every few millimetres. The necrosis caused by the salivary
injection extends for some distance from the point of puncture, and
these dead areas of cortex develop a severe canker especially when a
series of them coalesce. The canker persists as the stems grow and
mature, but the wound callus that is stimulated never entirely heals
the lesion. The result is the gnarled stem canker of tea described by
Leach and Smee.[13] The condition of the attacked branches further
deteriorates because of infection by fungi. Goodchild[14] has isolated
a *Phomopsis* and *Pestalotiopsis angusta* from old cankers. The bug
and the fungi between them work devastation on the wood and
promote serious die-back. This form of *Helopeltis* damage is distributed over tea districts in Malawi and Tanganyika and is potentially much more serious than that of *H. theivora*.

Both types of attack are lessened by careful control of shade. The
control of epidemics is effected by spraying or dusting with DDT.
An application is effective for a month to six weeks.

MITES

The behaviour of tea mites is very variable. A species economically important in one country or district is unimportant in another. The damage is often seasonal. With one exception mites are too small to be detected by the naked eye. Even though not readily seen, their lurking presence can be deduced from the presence of the skins which the growing nymph casts. Mites have oval compact bodies and usually have four pairs of legs, except the purple mite which has only two. Only the yellow mite damages the flush: the others cause defoliation or damage to mature leaves in differing degrees. Various formulations of sulphur sprays are effective in controlling mites, but, on tea, they can be used only when the bush is not in plucking because of the taint to the tea. Of the non-tainting acaricides Keltane has proved to be effective on all the species infesting tea. Although predators are known, their organization for biological control still remains to be worked out.[38]

"RED SPIDER"

Oligonychus coffeae (Nietner)
(Syn. *Tetranychus bioculatus: Metatetranychus bioculatus*)

This mite is widespread and occurs in most localities where tea is grown. Light[15] lists sixteen other tropical crops and plants upon which it has been found. In North-east India it is a serious pest.

Red spider is the only mite which is easily visible. The eggs are spherical and scarlet and the mite itself wine-coloured shading to bright red on the anterior parts. The male is smaller than the female and has a pointed posterior. The mites exist on the upper side of the leaf in clusters showing all stages of development.[1, 16] They spin a fine web over the surface of the leaf and their sucking activities produce red spots which may become so numerous as to give the whole leaf a brick-red appearance. Dry weather favours the development of attack which in a mild form may be dispersed by rain. But once a severe attack is prevalent it can persist during showery weather. Healthy bushes are less affected than weakly ones and according to Hainsworth[1] Assam jats of tea succumb less readily to attack than the China-hybrid types. The spread of the mites is certainly helped by the passage of pluckers and other workers through the tea. The presence of shade has a moderating effect. Severe attacks affect all types of tea equally, and lead to extensive defoliation. Cultural control is effected by maintenance of shade and good cultural conditions, by pruning, and by cleaning out and defoliation of pruned tea so as to reduce the food potential through the wintering season, if such there be. Where attacks are serious polysulphide sprays are effective against the mites, but to kill the eggs lime-sulphur is needed. Hainsworth referring to Assam conditions advocates two rounds of spraying as necessary for adequate control. The interval between these rounds is determined by the hatching period as influenced by season: it is longest between December and February and shortest in June and July.

PURPLE MITE

Calacarus carinatus (Green)
(Syn. *Calacarus adornatus* (Keifer), *Phytoptus carinatus* (Green),
Eriophyes carinatus (Green))

No host other than tea has been listed for the purple mite.[16] The body is purple with fine white ridges or keels. The life-cycle according to King is complete in nine to twenty days. Only mature leaves are affected and attacks are generally confined to periods of dry weather. The leaves attacked turn purple or bronze colour and numerous skin casts can be seen scattered over the surface. Defoliation is rare. The pest is not serious and disappears in the rainy season.

YELLOW MITE

Hemitarsonemus latus (Banks)
(Syn. *Tarsonemus translucens* (Green))

The body is parchment coloured with a clouded dorsal stripe: only six legs are developed.[17] Unlike the previous examples it prevails during cloudy wet weather and attacks only the young leaves, thus ruining the flush. Growth ceases, the leaves turn yellow and, on the under-surface, a rough brown discoloured area, which is quite characteristic, develops on either side of the mid-rib. When the bud is attacked, a rib may appear on the leaf, between the margin and the mid-rib, as the leaf unfolds. It is similar in appearance, though not in origin, to hail damage.

SCARLET MITE

Brevipalpus californicus (Banks)
(Syn. *Tenuipalpus obovatus* (Green), *Brevipalpus obovatus* (Donn.))

The appearance of scarlet mite is variable (Fig. 15). It may be bright scarlet or orange (in Indonesia it is known as orange mite); or it may be brownish black with a red spot at the posterior extremity. The mites adhere densely to the underside of the leaf near the mid-rib and produce a brown scurfy discoloration somewhat similar to that caused by yellow mite. The base of the leaf is particularly liable to damage and the injury there may result in the detachment of the whole leaf from the petiole. Green[17] at the turn of the century considered scarlet mite to be a very serious pest of tea in Ceylon causing defoliation, die-back and in severe instances complete death of the bush. Since then, though constantly reported it has figured only as a minor pest until recently (1955). Attacks are now of severity comparable to those recorded by Green and in some districts are increasing in severity. Popular opinion is inclined to link this increase with the use of copper sprays for the control of blister blight. Mites are attacked by entomogenous fungi which might be controlled by the copper fungicide, but there are difficulties in accepting the popular view. In the first place entomogenous fungi do not appear to exert an appreciable control of the mite population, and secondly scarlet mite is a dry weather pest, i.e. it flourishes at a time when spraying is habitually discontinued.

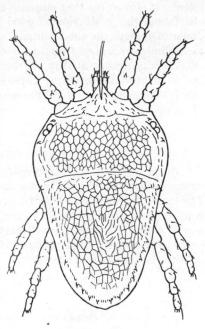

FIG. 15
The Scarlet Mite.
Brevipalpus californicus
(Banks)

PINK MITE

Acaphylla theae (Watt)

Pink mite has been reported from Assam but not elsewhere. Its body is continuously tapered from the head and it has only two pairs of legs. No eggs have ever been discovered. The outward and visible signs of attack are the pallid and sickly-looking appearance of the foliage, but the leaves are not shed. The margins of the leaves may be thickened or warted.[1] The pest is prevalent in dry weather.

Among the pests of local importance are the following:[1]

GREEN FLY

Empoasca flavescens (F.)

This leaf-hopper does a good deal of damage in Assam causing loss of crop and generally stunted growth. Elsewhere it is not prevalent. It has been credited with having a beneficial effect on the quality of tea. The validity of this claim has never been seriously tested. It is possible that climatic conditions favouring the fly may also favour the production of good-quality leaf. Also, some slowing down of growth, in good climatic conditions, is generally accepted as leading to improved quality and green-fly may have some such effect. Why similar quality characteristics do not appear when the leaf from bushes affected by capsids, aphids and thrips is manufactured is difficult to explain, if the manner of operation is as suggested.

THE TEA APHIS

Toxoptera aurantii (Boy.)

Clusters of this olive-brown aphis are occasionally to be found on young nursery plants and on the new shoots formed after pruning. The leaves become distorted and discoloured and internodal growth is affected. In the former case the damage done may be a serious matter calling for insecticidal treatment, but on mature bushes the pest is of very minor importance and disappears as the bushes develop, or with the onset of wet weather.

THRIPS

Dendothrips bispinosus (Bagn.)

Physothrips setiventris (Bagn.)

This is a well-established pest in Darjeeling. In Ceylon it is found in nurseries but not usually in the field. The insect makes longitudinal cuts in the buds which on expansion bear numerous corky lesions in consequence. In severe instances the attacks cause stunting similar to that produced by green-fly, aphis and other leaf-sucking species.

GREEN SCALE

Coccus viridis (Green)

This is an occasional pest more frequent in the drier zones. It is unsightly but does little harm. Its presence can usually be traced by reason of the sooty-mould fungus (*Meliola* species) which lives on the sweet secretion exuded by the scale and deposited on the leaves below. The fungus is entirely external to the leaf, but by cutting off light, probably affects the plant more adversely than the scale insect.

48. Factory tea-packing

49. Spreading leaf on withering tats (Indonesia)

50. Tea grading

STEM BORERS
SHOT-HOLE-BORER

Xyleborus fornicatus (Eichh.)
Xylosandrus compactus (Eichh.)

These bark-boring scolytid beetles are a serious pest in Ceylon, the former being the larger and more prevalent. Hainsworth[1] dismisses it as a curious and unimportant pest in India. They are, so far, unknown in Africa. No other tea pest has received more exhaustive investigation than *X. fornicatus*, initially by Jepson and Gadd[18] and subsequently in great detail by Gadd.[19, 20, 21, 22, 23, 24, 25, 26]

The damage is exclusively the work of the female which bores into the branches and excavates extensive and typical galleries about two millimetres in diameter. The beetle drives directly through to the wood and then turns and tunnels parallel to the cambial sheath. By the time her excavation is finished the gallery may be an almost complete circle. On occasions she drives across the pith to the opposite side before making the encircling manœuvre; and sometimes the peripheral portions of the gallery extend on both sides of the original shaft. In general, galleries may be simple or branched, but the living and generative cambium is untouched and the branch continues to grow in the normal manner. The point of entrance is frequently just beneath a dormant bud which is thereby aborted (Fig. 16).

The beetle lays her eggs and rears the resulting larvae in the galleries (Fig. 17). Their food is an ambrosial fungus (*Monacrosporium ambrosium*), growing on the gallery walls, spores of which are apparently carried by the beetle at the time of entrance.[27] After pupation the mature beetles emerge; the males being wingless. The female emerges from the gallery and the life-cycle is repeated with further depredations on the wood of growing tea. The whole cycle in days as worked out by Gadd is as follows:

Pre-oviposition	..	10
Incubation ..	..	7
Larvae	..	15
Pupae	..	8
Adult	..	5
Total ..	..	45

The extensive damage caused by shot-hole-borer is due to two causes. The excavation of the galleries weakens the rigidity of the branch and makes it very liable to breakage on account of the constant passage of pluckers and other workers through the tea. In

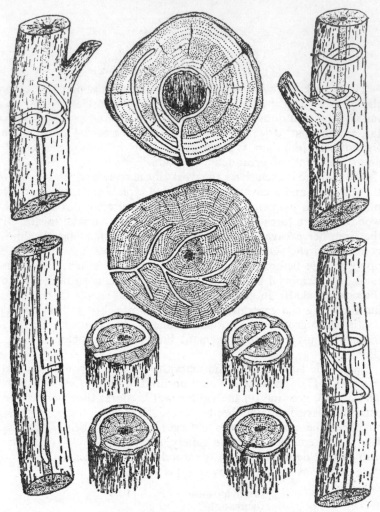

FIG. 16
Typical galleries made by the Shot-Hole-Borer Beetle, *Xyleborus fornicatus*
(Eichh.)

addition the high mortality of buds leads to die-back of broken
branches to the first viable bud. The combination of these two events
frequently leads to the death of entire branches. The beetle will bore
only into branches that have attained a girth suitable to house a
gallery, and the attack starts on new wood about a year old. Infesta-

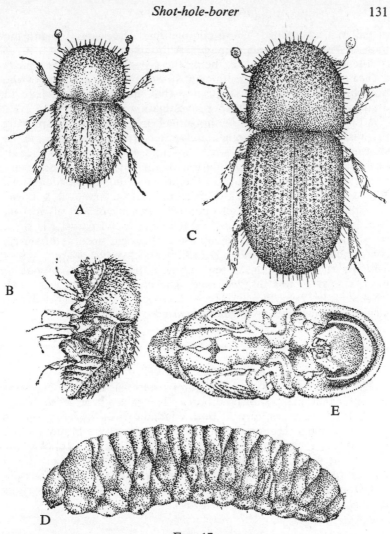

FIG. 17
The Shot-Hole-Borer, *Xyleborus fornicatus* (Eichh.)
A. and B. Male. C. Female. D. Larva. E. Pupa. (All × 30)

tion and breakage increase rapidly during the second year in accordance with compound interest law and decline in the third. Whether
this decline is due to the toughening of the older wood, or its inability
to sustain the ambrosia is not known, but the fall in breakages is
paralleled by the decline in population and by the increase in number

of galleries abandoned before completion. Nitrogenous manuring increases infestation and damage. Although the active growth of well-tended and manured tea helps the growth of callus that plugs a vacated gallery, this is insufficient to enhance the strength of the branch. Jepson's original suggestion that manuring would help to diminish damage was, as further investigation showed, invalid.

A high degree of control of shot-hole-borer is effected by spraying the bushes with dieldrin immediately after pruning. At this time the shot-hole-borer population is at a minimum and in the absence of flush the problem of contamination of the tea leaf by a persistent chemical is avoided. The use of dieldrin has untoward side effects. Whilst having no appreciable effect on tortrix larvae, it kills the parasite *Macrocentrus* which controls the incidence of tortrix. Because the natural re-establishment of the useful parasite is slow, supplementary spraying to check the consequent upsurge of tortrix is required. For this purpose D.D.T. is effective but is apt to upset a biological equilibrium and encourage mites. Dipterex is reported to be free from this disadvantage. The combination of these two treatments has been shown to be highly beneficial to the growth and yield of the treated tea (Cranham *et al.*).[28, 37]

RED BORER

Zeuzera coffeae (Nietn.)

The damage done by the red borer caterpillar is sometimes mistaken for that due to shot-hole-borer. The gallery is larger than that of shot-hole-borer, is open at both ends and runs the length of the attacked branch through the pith. The leaves of the branch wither and dry out even though the branch is unbroken. By splitting the branch the presence of the reddish caterpillar may be disclosed and its excreta in the form of red or yellowish ovoid pellets are generally to be found on the ground adjoining the bush. It is sometimes serious in nursery plants and young clearings.

TERMITES

Termites are troublesome pests that can cause the death of mature tea bushes and sizeable trees. Of those attacking live plants *Postelectrotermes militaris* does most damage. It enters roots and works its way upwards destroying the heart wood and migrates from root to root. *Neotermes greeni* and *Glyptotermes dilatatus* enter wounds or weak spots above ground. Live-wood termites live and nest in the attacked bush.

Scavenging termites such as *Hypotermes obscuriceps, Odonto-termes redemanni* and *O. horni* live in mounds or subterranean nests and construct galleries to the plants attacked. They live on tissues already dead from other causes. Some species, normally scavengers, may ring-bark a bush at the collar.

Treatment of the surrounding soil with a 1 per cent emulsion of dieldrin or aldrin is effective temporarily against scavengers, but not against live-wood species. Injection into the wide galleries of *Postelec-trotermes militaris* is possible but the galleries of other species are too narrow to make treatment successful.[39]

EELWORMS

Eelworm is the trivial name for a group of minute animals, the nematodes, that are widely distributed and some of which cause disease in plants, animals and human beings. They bear no relation-ship to earthworms. Their eel-like transparent bodies taper at both ends. The mouth parts have a sharp needle-like organ, the stylet, for boring into the tissues they invade. They are usually only a few millimetres long, and live freely in the soil. The female lays eggs which hatch into larvae that grow through stages of ecdysis to the mature adult.[29]

There are two genera which contain species that damage tea, *Meloidogyne*, the root-knot eelworm, and *Pratylenchus*, the root-lesion eelworm. *Meloidogyne javanica*, *M. arenaria* and *M. incognita* (var. *aerita*) have been reported in tea soils and behave similarly: they infect only young seedlings and are not continuously parasitic. *M. brevicauda* is truly parasitic.

The meadow eelworm *Pratylenchus loosi* is a very vicious parasite. The pin nematode *P. curvitatus* is under suspicion of parasitism.

ROOT-KNOT EELWORMS

Meloidogyne (Goeldi)

The commonest root-knot eelworm of tea has until recently always been referred to as *Heterodera marioni* (Cornu) Goodey. Since the transference of this species to a new genus which contains other species[30] it has been renamed *Meloidogyne javanica*.[36] The males and larvae have the typical eelworm shape. When mature the male is about one-and-a-half millimetres long. The female, which is smaller, changes appearance when about fifteen days old and eventually be-comes irregularly pear-shaped, like an old-fashioned alembic (Fig. 18). When root-tissues containing females are sectioned the worms can be seen with the naked eye as glistening pearly bodies embedded in the hypertrophied roots, and when gravid a large mass of eggs can be seen, under magnification, enclosed in an extruded sac.

The invasion of a root via the root-tip leads first to moderate swelling, but later produces multiple galls. It is characteristic of this species that it attacks only young seedlings up to about six months old. Older nursery plants and stumps or mature tea are unaffected. This is apparently due to failure to establish themselves after penetration of the older tissues, not to inability to enter them.[31]

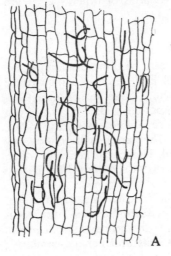  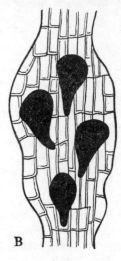

FIG. 18
Tea Root Eelworms.
A. *Pratylenchus pratensis* within rootlets
B. *Meloidogyne* sp. Female development and root swelling
C. *Meloidogyne* sp. Early root tip infection by larvae

Meloidogyne brevicauda (Loos)

In a few localities in Ceylon a root-knot eelworm was observed to be prevalent in patches on mature tea. The possibilities that this discovery suggested were three: (1) that the field had been planted with affected seedlings and that the eelworm had persisted; (2) that a modification of the species formerly known as *Heterodera marioni* had occurred which was capable of parasitizing mature roots as well as young ones; (3) that the eelworm was of a different species. The latter possibility proved to be correct.[32]

The new species is similar to the other root-knot eelworm from which it is distinguished by coarser striations, and blunter tail in the larvae.

MEADOW EELWORMS

Pratylenchus pratensis (de Man, 1881 ; Goffart, 1929)
Pratylenchus coffeae (Zimmerman, 1898 ; Goodey, 1951)

The meadow eelworm is a much more serious pest than that causing root-knot. It is smaller (about 0·5 mm. average) and not so pointed at head and tail. It is widely distributed in Eastern and Western hemispheres and in both temperate and tropical climates.[29]

The nematodes attack young feeding-roots near the tip and also the older thicker roots. They move through the cells and kill them : clusters of them can most easily be found at the junction of dead and living tissue by carefully stripping away the cortex and examining its underside (Fig. 18). They do not enter the wood, neither do they cause galls or swellings, but they effectively kill feeding-roots. An affected plant has a sickly, thin appearance, and the leaves are pale and yellowish. Before the real cause of the ailment was discovered these bushes were often described as having a type of witch's broom. These symptoms can be caused by other pests, e.g. red spider, and identification by microscopic examination is always necessary. The paucity of young roots and die-back at the tip are additional symptoms that help preliminary identification in the field.[33]

The eelworm feeds, breeds and spends most of its time in the roots of the plant, but is sufficiently mobile to travel from bush to bush in a free state. The spread of the disease is assisted by damp soils. The very severe damage eelworms do is not due to their effect on the cortex of mature roots so much as their wholesale destruction of feeding-roots. Gadd has isolated as many as 20,000 eelworms from one two-year-old seedling.[34] In a matter of ten years yields may be halved as a result of their ravages.[33]

EELWORM CONTROL

Eelworms have proved to be very troublesome creatures to control, and the only satisfactory method is crop rotation that eliminates species that are susceptible, thus denying them the basic needs of food and shelter. This is obviously impossible as regards perennial crops such as tea. The interplanting of highly susceptible plant species as traps is of limited usefulness, first, because eelworms tend to become specialized as regards host, and second, because unless the trap is removed at the critical time, i.e. before a new generation is liberated, the last state is liable to be worse than the first. On the other hand, the web of fungal hyphae that ramifies in the soil when organic matter is undergoing decomposition, is an effective trap for males and larvae that are mobile, and hence intensive green manuring, though not providing complete control, has been found to be of practical value.[35] Some species and strains of plants are less susceptible than others and hope of control rests largely on the development of such immune types.[31]

There are two short-term measures that have recently met with a moderate success. The first is the use of toxic fumigants. The research stations in Ceylon and Assam have reported two products as promising, namely Nemagon and Nematox, both in their lethal effect on eelworms and as regards the accompanying improvement in plant growth on the treated plots. Whether such treatment would be economic where large-scale infestation occurs remains to be determined, but as a method of containing a developing attack it has the advantage of offering an immediately effective remedy.

The cultivation of marigolds, *Tagetes patula* and *T. erecta*, has a significant effect on the eelworm population.[40,41] These plants do not merely act as traps in the sense previously referred to. The eelworms invade their roots but cannot survive. The controlling effect applies to both the types of eelworm known to affect tea. Used as a sanitary crop on newly opened tea land, before planting tea, or interplanted with established tea, marigolds could be used effectively and inexpensively on large acreages.

In general, the most profitable course to adopt for limiting eelworm infestation is (*a*) to eliminate shade trees that are known to be highly susceptible, (*b*) to use both green manures and marigolds as complementary crops having a deterrent effect, (*c*) to use fumigation as a nursery treatment and to deal with limited attacks over a small area, and (*d*) in the case of *Meloidogyne* attacks in nurseries, to abandon an infected site if other methods prove ineffective.

REFERENCES

1. HAINSWORTH, E., *Tea Pests and Diseases*, Heffer, Cambridge, 1952.
2. Tea Research Institute of East Africa, Annual Report, 1954, 40.
3. KING, C. B. R., *Tea Quarterly*, 1933, 6, 153.
4. GADD, C. H., ibid., 1941, 14, 93.
5. ——, *Ceylon Journal of Science B.*, 1946, 23, 67.
6. AUSTIN, G. D., *Tea Quarterly*, 1931, 4, 74.
7. Tea Research Institute of Ceylon, Annual Report, 1953, 52.
8. GADD, C. H. and FONSEKA, W. T., *Ceylon Journal of Science B.*, 1945, 23, 9.
9. Tea Research Institute of Ceylon, Annual Report, 1952, 43.
10. ——, Annual Report, 1950, 47.

11. WATT, G. and MANN, H. H., *The Pests and Blights of the Tea Plant*, 2nd edn., Government Printer, Calcutta, 1903.
12. SMEE, C., *The Tea Mosquito Bug in Nyasaland*, Dept. of Agric. Bull. No. 4 (Ento. Series). 1928
13. LEACH, R. and SMEE, C., *Ann. app. Biol.*, 1933, **20**, 691.
14. Tea Research Institute of East Africa, Annual Report, 1953, 30.
15. LIGHT, S., *Trop. Agriculturist*, 1927–8, **68**, 229.
16. KING, C. B. R., *Tea Quarterly*, 1936, **9**, 144.
17. GREEN, E. E., Royal Botanic Gardens (Ceylon) Circular, 1900, Series 1, No. 17.
18. JEPSON, F. P. and GADD, C. H., Dept. of Agric., Ceylon. Bull. 78.
19. GADD, C. H., *Tea Quarterly*, 1941, **14**, 5.
20. ——, ibid., 1941, **14**, 132.
21. ——, ibid., 1942, **15**, 31.
22. ——, ibid., 1943, **16**, 6.
23. ——, ibid., 1943, **16**, 30.
24. ——, ibid., 1944, **17**, 2.
25. ——, ibid., 1946–7, **18**, 114.
26. ——, ibid., 1949, **20**, 61.
27. GADD, C. H. and LOOS, C. A., *Trans. Brit. mycol. Soc.*, 1948, **31**, 13.
28. CRANHAM, J. E., *et al.*, *Tea Quarterly*, 1963, **34**, 127.
29. GOODEY, T., *Plant Parasitic Nematodes*, Methuen, London, 1933.
30. CHITWOOD, B. G., *Proc. helm. Soc., Wash.*, 1949, **16**, 90.
31. GADD, C. H. and LOOS, C. A., *Tea Quarterly*, 1946, **18**, 3.
32. LOOS, C. A., *Proc. hel. Soc., Wash.*, 1953, **20**, 83.
33. GADD, C. H., *Tea Quarterly*, 1939, **12**, 131.
34. ——, ibid., 1947, **19**, 61.
35. DUDDINGTON, C. L., *The Friendly Fungi*, Faber, London, 1957.
36. LOOS, C. A., *Tea Quarterly*, 1953, **24**, 34.
37. CRANHAM, J. E., *et al.*, *Tea Quarterly*, 1962, **33**, 196.
38. ——, ibid., 1962, **33**, 189.
39. RANAWEERA, D. J. W., ibid., 1962, **33**, 88.
40. VISSER, T., and VYTHILINGAM, M. K., ibid., 1959, **30**, 30.
41. HUTCHINSON, M. J., Tea Research Institute of Ceylon, Report, 1962, Part II, 70.

Chapter XII

THE CHEMISTRY OF THE TEA LEAF AND OF ITS MANUFACTURE

Inorganic Constituents—The Nitrogen Compounds—Carbohydrate and Associated Compounds—The Polyphenols— Pigments—Enzymes—Vitamins—Fermentation—The Question of Quality.

THE chemical composition of the tea leaf is of interest mainly because of the reactions that take place during its manufacture. Of obvious importance are the compounds that contribute to the strength, colour, pungency, flavour and stimulating properties of the beverage.

Besides these, the leaf contains the normal constituents found in all plant tissues and of these some are present in quantities that distinguish tea from the general run of plants.

INORGANIC CONSTITUENTS

The inorganic constituents are found mainly as salts in the cell sap. Those of particular note are as follows:

Aluminium. The phenomenon of aluminium accumulation has already been dealt with in some detail and is mentioned again only for the sake of completeness.

Manganese. Tea foliage also accumulates manganese in appreciable quantities. The green tint of ashed tea leaf is due to the presence of manganese salts. The concentration increases with age of leaf in a manner similar to that of aluminium. Chenery[1] reports values as high as nine thousand parts per million (0·90 per cent) in mature leaves from Malawi. Ordinary flush plucked in the field contains up to nineteen hundred parts per million in Kenya samples. These figures are high in comparison with most other plants, but no toxic symptoms were produced.[2]

Potassium. In concentration this element ranks highest amongst the mineral constituents: the young foliage is the richest. The content is noticeably increased by potash manuring, in some instances to an extent that indicates luxury consumption. Average figures compiled over long periods lie within the range 1·35 to 1·76.[3, 4] Where luxury

138

consumption is operative the percentage rises to as much as 2·0. De Haan and Schoorel[5] place the absolute potassium deficiency levels below about 0·6 per cent on the dry matter.

Calcium is the next most abundant mineral constituent with a concentration round about 0·5 to 0·7 per cent.[2]

Magnesium. Deficiency symptoms have been reported from Indonesia, Ceylon, East Africa and the former Belgian Congo.[6] The foliar symptoms show chlorotic intervenous areas with main veins remaining green. Frequently at the leaf base an inverted V-shaped area also remains green. Leaf samples from Indonesia, Uganda and the Congo show that for deficient leaves the Mg content is below 0·2 per cent and the K/Mg ratio above 10. These figures agree with corresponding ones on other crops.

Iron. The iron content of tea is very variable and can be quite remarkably low in leaf that has a high manganese content. Child reports values lower than 100 parts per million.[7]

Copper. This element is of special importance to tea because of the role it plays in the fermentation process. As far as the efficiency of physiological processes is concerned the quantities present are more than adequate, but very variable amounts are reported from the various tea areas.

Indian teas with contents (p.p.m.) in the low thirties; Ceylon samples containing 25–30 p.p.m., and a solitary Japanese sample (62 p.p.m.) are all richer in copper than samples from Africa and Malaya, with figures round about 15 p.p.m., except those from areas deficient in sulphur (which is closely associated with copper geologically), where values are as low as 7 p.p.m.[8, 9]

Phosphorus. The highest concentrations are in the young leaves which show a good deal of variation in content. Manuring with phosphates increases the amount in the foliage till luxury consumption is observed.

The following table gives Lamb's[10] proximate analysis to which a number of items have been added:

INORGANIC CONSTITUENTS OF TEA

	Per cent of dry weight			Per cent of dry weight
Potassium	1·76		Sulphur	0·088
Calcium	0·41		Aluminium	0·069
Phosphorus	0·32		Sodium	0·030
Magnesium	0·22		Silicon	0·024
Iron	0·15		Zinc	0·003
Manganese	0·12		Copper	0·002

The total ash content of leaf plucked for manufacture varies from 4·5 to 5·0 per cent.

THE NITROGEN COMPOUNDS

Average quality leaf, plucked for manufacture, usually contains from 4·5 to 5·0 per cent of nitrogen in terms of the dry weight. Of this quantity, about three-quarters consists of proteins and amino-acids that are basic constituents of the protoplasm. The remaining quarter is from the alkaloid caffeine of which there is about 2·5 to 4·5 per cent in the dry leaf. Roughly a quarter of the amino-acid and protein nitrogen is soluble so that, adding this to the caffeine, nearly half the nitrogen in tea leaf is found in the brew when tea is made. The processes of manufacture do not alter substantially the quantities of soluble protein and caffeine that are extractable except that soluble protein is decreased by long withers. On the other hand withering does increase somewhat the proportion of amino-acids in the leaf. Russian workers associate the production of leucine and phenyla-lanine in withered leaf with the development of aroma. By adding amino-acids to extracts of hot tea they claim to have produced a variety of aromas. These, they postulate are associated with alde-hydes derived from amino-acids on oxidation by quinone.[48, 49] The most abundant amino-acid derivative in tea is theanine which con-stitutes something like 1·5 to 2·0 per cent of the dry matter of tea, and roughly one sixth of this percentage to the nitrogen content. It has been identified as N-ethyl-γ-glutamine.[11] Typical figures from a series of analyses that illustrate the foregoing broad generalizations are: total nitrogen 4·5 per cent: soluble protein and amino-acid nitrogen 0·92 per cent; insoluble nitrogen 2·51 per cent; caffeine nitrogen 1·07 per cent (caffeine percentage 3·71).[12]

Included in the protoplasmic proteins are various enzymes which play so important a role in bringing about fermentation during manufacture. The characteristic enzyme of the tea leaf is associated with the chloroplasts of the leaf.

CARBOHYDRATE AND ASSOCIATED COMPOUNDS

The cellulosic constituents of tea leaf play no chemical part in the preparation of tea and therefore call for no comment. Sugars and starch are consistently found in tea leaf but only in small quantities. Lamb and Sreerangachar give the following percentages: Sugars, 0·73–1·41; Starch, 0·82–2·96.[13] Cartwright and Roberts found indica-tions of ten sugars on their chromatograms of made-tea extracts. The presence of glucose, fructose and sucrose is certain, with a high probability that arabinose and ribose are also constituents of the carbohydrate group.[14]

The position as regards starch is peculiar, as it is not freely translocatable. When tea leaves are covered up, after the traditional manner employed in physiological experiments, no appreciable diminution in starch granules in the cells is noted, even after a period of fourteen days.

Starch in large quantities is stored in the root system of tea and consequently the products of photosynthesis must be correspondingly prolific. The mechanism of translocation has never been worked out, nor is it known whether the characteristic polyphenol compounds that abound in tea play an essential part in the process.

Lipids occur in the general protoplasm but it is not known whether they have any significant part to play in the manufacturing process.

Pectins are present in quite large but very variable amounts in tea flush. The quantity varies according to the component parts of which the flush is made up. It is highest in the stalk (7·6 per cent) and in the first leaf (6·1 per cent) and lower in the bud and older leaves. It breaks down in the course of manufacture to form pectic acid and methyl alcohol. There is evidence that the pectic acid jelly, by forming a coating over the macerated and fermenting leaf, inhibits to some extent the progress of polyphenol oxidation in its initial stages.[15]

THE POLYPHENOLS

The most important and characteristic components of tea leaf are the polyphenols in the cell sap which undergo a series of chemical changes when the leaf is macerated during manufacture. Those occurring in tea are derivatives of gallic acid and of catechin. The best-known gallic acid derivatives are the tannins, so-called from their property of tanning hides and thereby converting them to leather; consequently the tea polyphenols were long classed as tannins. This is a misnomer since the primary polyphenols in tea have no tanning properties and the term is better avoided. The polyphenols, like the alcohols, are a very large class and their properties and derivatives differ widely. There is no more essential similarity in constitution and properties between the true tannins and the so-called tea-tannins than exists, for example, between potable alcohol and glycerine, both of which are alcohols.

Traditional and chromatographic methods of chemical analysis have so far separated more than a dozen distinguishable compounds with chemical configurations based on catechin and gallic acid. Not all of these can be confidently assumed to occur naturally in tea leaf: some are undoubtedly isomeric artifacts produced during the processes of extraction and analysis. The elucidation of the nature of these compounds is due to Tsujimura,[16, 17] and Oshima[18] in Japan, and to Roberts[19, 20, 21] and Bradfield,[22, 23, 24] and their co-workers. Roberts and Wood list four catechins which they provisionally conclude occur naturally in tea leaf. These are: (1) (+)—catechin, (2) (+)—gallocatechin, (3) (−)—*epi*catechin and (4) (−)—*epi*gallocatechin. In a more recent review of the chemistry of tea fermentation Roberts[21] adds to these the galloyl esters of (−)—*epi*catechin and (−)—*epi*gallocatechin. The fundamental constitutions of the catechins and gallocatechins are

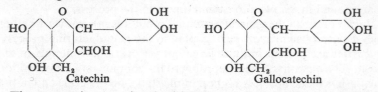

OH CH$_2$ OH CH$_2$
Catechin   Gallocatechin

The properties associated with tea as a beverage are associated with the products of the enzymic oxidation of these catechins and their subsequent modification during the manufacturing process.

Numerous analogous polyphenolic compounds have been isolated in addition to these fundamental ones of which the chief are rutin, quercetin, chlorogenic acid (the galloyl ester of caffeic acid) and theogallin, the corresponding ester of quinic acid.[25]

There are several factors that affect the polyphenol content of tea leaf and the resulting tea. The concentration in the component parts of the flush decreases as they develop. In arbitrary units the average amounts, determined as "total oxidizable matter" are: bud 100; first leaf 96; first stalk 94; second leaf 93; second stalk 75; third leaf 80.[26] There are also seasonal changes in the polyphenol content of the flush as a whole. Evans,[27] Shaw[28] and Child[26] have followed the seasonal trends in detail and have found that polyphenol contents are higher in the slower growing period of dry weather and ample sunshine. The inhibition of crop during monsoon rains is accompanied by low values of total oxidizable matter. The "tipping leaf," i.e. the first leaf harvested after pruning, is always lower in polyphenol content than that of subsequent flushes. Similarly, tea grown under shade is of lower polyphenol content. Contrary to common opinion there is no evidence that the proper use of artificial fertilizers (particularly nitrogenous fertilizers) has any consistent or deleterious effect.[29, 30]

PIGMENTS

The chlorophyll of the leaf enters into the chemical reactions of tea manufacture and is decomposed in the process of fermentation. Tea leaf also contains red and yellow pigments derived from anthocyanins and flavones. Of the latter quercetin, a flavonol, has already been mentioned. Some bushes have excessive quantities of anthocyanin, the abundance of which is a genetical characteristic. A red pigment has been separated from a bush in whose young leaves the anthocyanin masked the normal green of the chlorophyll, and a clone of such bushes has been established in Ceylon.[31] The yellow flavone pigments present in tea leaf are capable of being changed into anthocyanins to which they are nearly related. A notable instance of this modification is sometimes caused by blister blight; the translucent spot which appears before the hymenium ruptures the epidermis being pink in colour instead of yellow.[31]

ENZYMES

The oxidation of tea polyphenols on exposure to air is exceedingly slow unless brought about by the activity of the appropriate enzyme. Whilst it is not unlikely that more than one enzyme is involved, the major reaction is accomplished by a specific oxidase, a protein of which the prosthetic element is copper. Successive purification of the crude enzyme in bulk has shown that its activity is proportionally increased as the apparent copper concentration increases.[32] The oxidase appears to have both a water-soluble and an insoluble component of which the latter is the more potent, though whether this distinction is real is not definitely established. The difference may be accountable to the difficulty in extracting the enzyme from intact chloroplasts.

The specificity of the enzyme in oxidizing hydroxyl groups in the ortho-position was demonstrated by Lamb and Sreerangachar.[33] The rate of oxidation is a function of the amount of enzyme present, and its activity is affected by the accumulation of the products of fermentation. The activity of the oxidase varies with the season, being generally higher in periods of dry weather.

The individual portions of the flush differ widely, and reasonably consistently, in enzyme activity. In contradistinction to the polyphenols in the leaf the enzyme activity shows no marked and progressive decline from the younger to the older portions. What is apparent is the much higher enzyme activity of the stalk and the marked superiority of the bud over the fully expanded leaves. Using the bud activity as the standard the relative values are for a typical flush: bud 100; first leaf 56; first stalk 139; second leaf 51; second stalk 99; third leaf 56.[34]

Although, as previously mentioned, the copper is a characteristic constituent of the enzyme its concentration is not, in general, a reliable index of enzyme activity. High enzyme activity of the stalk is not accompanied by a correspondingly high value of enzymic copper in comparison with that of the leaves.[34] Reviewing the disparate copper contents of flush from the various tea-growing countries, this lack of uniformity between copper content and enzyme activity makes it impossible to dogmatize on the causes of slow or imperfect fermentation in regions where copper content is low. Nevertheless encouraging practical results have been obtained in Malawi by spraying copper salts onto the foliage of tea as an aid to fermentation. Conversely, in Ceylon, a clone of tea has been established from a non-fermenting mother-bush, whose copper content is much lower than the general run of values.

Of other enzymes present in tea leaf mention must be made of a peroxidase capable under the requisite conditions of oxidizing the catechins, but it is now agreed that it plays no important part in tea fermentation.[35]

The pectins are decomposed during manufacture by a pectase that behaves in a manner similar to that operative in citrus fruits.

Sreerangachar attributes the breakdown of chlorophyll fermentation to an unidentified enzyme and suggests that there is subsequent oxidation by ortho-quinone.[36]

VITAMINS

Riboflavin (Vitamin B_2) is present in tea leaf and persists during manufacture and storage. As a source of riboflavin tea has, weight for weight, about half the value of yeast and 80 per cent of it passes into the cup when tea is brewed.[37] Ascorbic acid (Vitamin C) is also a constituent of tea leaf but is oxidized during the fermentation process in the manufacture of black tea.

FERMENTATION

As has been indicated previously the most important chemical process occurring in tea manufacture is the oxidation of the polyphenols by atmospheric oxygen with the help of an oxidase. It is a time-honoured convention to refer to this and subsequent reactions as a fermentation process. The term covers a large number of dissimilar chemical reactions initiated by enzyme activity, but because of its practical use in commercial manufacturing procedure it will be used here and subsequently to describe the whole range of reactions that are started by the enzymic oxidation.

The basic change brought about by fermentation is the production from the catechins of *o*-benzoquinone derivatives.

The oxidation of the individual polyphenols in the complex does not occur simultaneously but successively and in ordinary manufacture does not proceed to completion: thus manufactured tea frequently contains chromatographically detectable amounts of (−)—epi-catechin and (+)—catechin. The finished product also shows quite large quantities of gallic acid derived from the breakdown of the aforementioned gallic acid esters. The compounds extractable by infusion of the made tea are fractionable into those which are soluble in ethyl acetate and those that are not, the former being the polymers of relatively low molecular weight and the latter the more complicated compounds. This fractionation affords a clue to the problem of quality in tea which will be referred to in the next section.[38, 39]

Roberts[44, 45, 50] and his associates have investigated the complicated chain of reactions taking place during tea manufacture thereby clarifying and simplifying them. Of the six catechin derivatives naturally occurring in tea leaf (p. 142) only two are of major importance, epigallocatechin and its gallate. After the oxidation of these catechins to o-benzoquinone derivatives the subsequent changes are now seen to be simpler than was formerly thought to be the case. Only two molecules are concerned and the structurally rearranged compound is thus more accurately referred to as a dimer than as a polymer. Three variants are possible formed from (a) a pair of epigallocatechin molecules; (b) a pair of epigallocatechin gallate molecules; and (c) a hybrid pair consisting of one epigallocatechin molecule and one of epigallocatechin gallate. These rearranged pairs are designated bis-flavanols, the term flavanol in this context being synonymous with catechin.

These bis-flavanols are capable of further reaction with orthoquinone products already present and the resulting new compounds are *theaflavins* (T F in brief). An additional oxidation, not controlled by enzyme action, transforms these theaflavins to *thearubigins* (T R). The complete chain of reactions may be set out as follows:

epigallocatechin and/or its gallate
 ↓ enzymic oxidation
orthobenzoquinone products
 ↓ dimerization
bis-flavanols
 ↓ condensation with orthoquinones
Theaflavins
 ↓ non-enzymic oxidation
Thearubigins

These reactions do not proceed to completion during normal

manufacture and the finished black tea contains both theaflavins and thearubigins. As the period of fermentation is prolonged the proportion of thearubigins increases.[45]

Fermentation time (hours)	1	2	3	4	5
TF per cent	.. 1·61	1·46	1·34	1·27	1·17
TR per cent	.. 13·0	16·6	16·6	16·7	17·1

Orthodox methods of rolling give lower TR/TF than maceration methods.

THE QUESTION OF QUALITY

There are many factors that determine the quality of tea. Some are uncontrollable whilst others can be elucidated in terms of biochemistry. The ideal goal for biochemical research as it applies to tea is to define precisely those processes and constituents that promote good quality with a view to using these objective criteria, as far as possible, in place of the subjective, albeit skilled, estimate of the tea-taster. The attainment of this ideal lies in the distant future, but valuable help can be given to the tea industry on the basis of knowledge so far gained.

As the preceding summary of chemical changes makes abundantly clear, the ordinary cup of tea contains a mixture of substances of different constitution with differing properties. The first task was to separate them. Bradfield [38, 39] established the fact that those substances which would dissolve in ethyl acetate were conspicuously associated with bright orange liquors of marked astringency, and creamed down on addition of caffeine. He accordingly concluded that a high proportion of ethyl acetate soluble material in a tea sample was a useful indication of its superior quality. Teas of this nature are produced by short, efficient fermentation. Roberts's researches showed why this was so, for the ethyl acetate extracts contained the whole of the theaflavins which give the bright colour and brisk sensation on the palate. As theaflavins were changed to thearubigins colour deepened, liquors were less bright and of diminished astringency and strength. Obviously a tea distinguished for colour, strength, briskness and flavour would be one which had a TR/TF ratio of fairly limited range. Moreover since the TR content is normally ten times as great as TF, fermentation methods and times would need careful regulation. A tea with a low TR/TF ratio (10–12) has the best quality, other things being equal. These other factors now require consideration.

The prime consideration in quality of tea is the nature of the leaf that is plucked. Good tea is the product of good leaf in the first place, and by good leaf is meant leaf of high polyphenol content, high enzymic activity, and physically in a condition that allows the tissues to be adequately worked on in the manufacturing processes in order that the best conditions possible can be procured for the essential chemical changes to occur. The preceding discussions throw light upon the reasons why coarse plucking, i.e. taking flush shoots of more than bud and two or at the most three leaves, militates against the production of tea of good quality. Not only will the average polyphenol content be low, but the maturer and more lignified leaf will not easily macerate, nor its cells distort during manufacture to an extent that will give free access of air to the fermenting mass, and intimate mingling of polyphenol and enzyme.

The rhythm of growth of the tea bush also affects quality. The Ceylon workers have shown that under the traditional régime of long pruning cycles the quality of the leaf improves with age from pruning at any rate up to the fourth year. Under the annual pruning régime in Assam "second flush" and "autumnal" teas are of better quality than "rains" teas. Seasonal changes in quality are also well recognized as being associated with slower growth and higher concentrations of the reactants in the leaf. Damaged leaf is also inimical to good quality, because it starts uncontrolled fermentation, and, during carriage and storage, attains temperatures that affect the train of subsequent processes.

The effects of cultural treatments on quality have received constant investigation but without any very positive results. Mann, in the early investigations at Tocklai, inclined to the view that phosphate status of the soil was a determining factor but this view has not been further substantiated.[40] The well-recognized association of quality with slow growth illustrated both by seasonal quality periods and by the superiority of high-grown Ceylon teas over those of low and medium elevations has rendered lavish manuring suspect as a contributory cause of poor quality. Eden and Evans[30] however found no significant differences between teas receiving no nitrogen and those manured with 40 lb. of nitrogen per acre in respect of percentage extract and total oxidizable matter. Soluble nitrogen of all kinds and in particular caffeine were slightly higher in manured teas as was also the ash content, but to extents that were technologically unimportant. There were no differences whatever between the ratings of teas manured with equivalent but different types of nitrogen whether from organic or inorganic sources.[30] Up to a limit of 80 lb. per acre of nitrogen, manured and unmanured teas were indistinguishable in Ceylon when subjected to the traditional tea-tasting techniques.

Harrison and his associates[41, 42] detect deterioration when nitrogen applications approach 120 lb. of nitrogen per acre in Assam. On the other hand recent work in East Africa has raised the problem in a different form. Visitors from other tea-producing countries consistently remark upon the yellow-green appearance of tea flush particularly in the Kenya highlands. Not every bush is affected but the general effect is undeniable. Todd[43] investigated the composition of green and yellow-green leaf and, in a series of tests, found the latter to be superior in respect of extract and total oxidizable matter (i.e. polyphenol content), but very inferior in nitrogen content. When the two kinds of leaf were fermented the colour development in the yellow leaf was superior both in intensity and in the brightness of the red coloration, and this difference was reflected in the extracts. The superiority was confirmed in tasting assessments. Wight and Gilchrist[51] have extended the search for quality correlations by relating the strength and flavour of tea to four measurable characteristics of the growing leaf. They choose crop yield per bush (C); hairiness of leaf (H); phloem index, the frequency of occurrence of calcium oxalate crystals in the phloem tissue of the petiole (Pi); and the ratio of xylem to phloem vessels in the vascular bundles (Vb). The equations they arrive at are linear.

$$\text{Quality} = -27 + 0.06C + 5.5H + 0.16 \text{ Pi} + 50Vb$$
$$\text{Strength} = +22 + 0.11C + 4.5H + 0.05 \text{ Pi} - 22Vb$$

The most consistent relationship disclosed by the equations, that concerned with hairiness, is reflected in the coefficient of H in the first equation. It does not differ substantially from the corresponding value in the equation for strength. The other noticeable features of these equations are the signs of the Vb coefficients which indicate contrary influence as regards quality and strength. Taken together, these four characteristics account for the ascertained variations in strength and quality, over the range of samples tested, with adequate statistical accuracy. The importance of each individiual characteristic requires further examination.

The debate on the effect of shade impinges on the question of quality, the common opinion being that excessive shade is deleterious to quality. Shade could conceivably influence the delicate balance of polyphenolic substances synthesized in the leaf, but investigations do not support the supposition. Different clones have different proportions of the two primary catechins, epigallocatechin and its gallate, but shade produces no differential effect. The same is true for cultural treatments or difference in locality. The constant ratio is determined genetically.

During the course of tea manufacture there are reactions taking place quite distinct from those connected with polyphenol oxidation. Tea leaf, in common with other vegetable matter, supports at the time of plucking a strictly moderate bacterial flora when dry. This is kept in check by the withering process. But if the leaf is wet the initial count, though still moderate, is greater, and during the drying-off process increases threefold. When subjected to long and inadequate withering the increase in bacterial flora is rapid. The products of tea fermentation have a marked bacteriocidal action and in well-made tea the bacterial proliferation is negligible. The bacteria concerned are medically harmless but certain of them, if allowed to develop, have a deleterious effect on the quality of the tea produced, rendering the liquor soft and characterless.[47]

An additional adventitious factor affecting quality is the moisture content of the finished tea. To anticipate the more detailed account in the following chapter, fresh dry tea should have a moisture content of about 3 per cent. Being by nature hygroscopic tea will pick up moisture in sorting, packing and storage if atmospheric conditions are not controlled. By the time a tea has acquired a moisture content of about 9–10 per cent the pungency of the brew is affected, and at higher moisture contents moulds are likely to develop which impart a musty taint to the dry tea and the liquors.[46]

REFERENCES

1. CHENERY, E. M., *Plant and Soil*, 1955, 6, 175.
2. Tea Research Institute of East Africa, Annual Report, 1954, 38.
3. EDEN, T., *Emp. J. exp. Agric.*, 1944, 12, 177.
4. PORTSMOUTH, G. B., *Tea Quarterly*, 1953, 24, 79.
5. DE HAAN, I. and SCHOOREL, A. F., *Archief v.d. Theecultuur*, 1940, 14, 43.
6. CHENERY, E. M. and SCHOENMAEKERS, J., *E. Afr. agric. J.*, 1959, 25, 25.
7. Tea Research Institute of East Africa, Annual Report, 1955, 26.
8. RAMASWAMY, M. S., *Tea Quarterly*, 1960, 31, 76.
9. CHILD, R., *Tropical Agriculture*, 1955, 32, 100.
10. LAMB, J., Tea Research Institute of Ceylon, Bull. No. 31, 1949, 27.
11. CARTWRIGHT, R. A., ROBERTS, E. A. H. and WOODS, D. J., *J. Sci. Fd Agric.*, 1954, 5, 597.
12. Tea Research Institute of East Africa, Annual Report, 1954, 33.
13. LAMB, J. and SREERANGACHAR, H. B., *Biochem. J.*, 1940, 34, 1472.
14. CARTWRIGHT, R. A. and ROBERTS, E. A. H., *J. Sci. Fd Agric.*, 1954, 5, 600.
15. LAMB, J. and RAMASWAMY, M. S., *J. Sci. Fd Agric.*, 1958, 9, 46, 51.
16. TSUJIMURA, M., *Sci. Pap. Inst. phys. chem. Res.* (*Tokyo*), 1929, 10, 253.
17. TSUJIMURA, M., ibid., 1935, 26, 186.
18. OSHIMA, Y. and GOMA, T., *J. agric. chem. Soc. Japan*, 1933, 9, 948.

19. ROBERTS, E. A. H. and WOODS, D. J., *Biochem. J.*, 1951, **49**, 414.
20. ——, ibid., 1953, **53**, 332.
21. ROBERTS, E. A. H., *J. Sci. Fd Agric.*, 1952, **3**, 193.
22. BRADFIELD, A. E., PENNEY, M. and WRIGHT, W. B., *J. chem. Soc.*, 1947, 42.
23. BRADFIELD, A. E. and PENNEY, M., *J. Chem. Soc.*, 1948, 2249.
24. BRADFIELD, A. E. and BATE-SMITH, E. C., *Biochem. biophys. Acta*, 1950, **4**, 441.
25. CARTWRIGHT, R. A. and ROBERTS, E. A. H., *J. Sci. Fd Agric.*, 1954, **5**, 593.
26. Tea Research Institute of East Africa, Annual Report, 1953, 33.
27. EVANS, D. I., 1929, Tea Research Institute of Ceylon, Bulletin No. 3.
28. SHAW, W. S., *Theotannin*, Part 1, 2nd edn., United Planters Assn., S. India, Bulletin No. 4, 1935.
29. EDEN, T., *Emp. J. exp. Agric.*, 1933, **1**, 297.
30. ——, ibid., 1935, **3**, 115.
31. Tea Research Institute of Ceylon, Annual Report, 1947, 46.
32. SREERANGACHAR, H. B., *Biochem. J.*, 1943, **37**, 661.
33. LAMB, J. and SREERANGACHAR, H. B., *Biochem. J.*, 1940, **34**, 1485.
34. Tea Research Institute of East Africa, Annual Report, 1953, 37, 39.
35. ROBERTS, E. A. H., *Biochem. J.*, 1941, **35**, 1209.
36. SREERANGACHAR, H. B., *Current Science*, 1943, **12**, 205.
37. Tea Research Institute of Ceylon, Annual Report, 1947, 47.
38. BRADFIELD, A. E., *Chemistry and Industry*, 1946, **24**, 242.
39. BRADFIELD, A. E. and PENNEY, M., *J. Soc. chem. Ind., London*, 1944, **63**, 306.
40. MANN, H. H., *Tea Soils*, Commonwealth Bur. Soil Sci., Tech. Comm. No. 32.
41. HARRISON, C. J., *Experiments on the Quality of Tea*, Indian Tea Assn., Calcutta, 1936.
42. HARRISON, C. J., BOSE, S. S. and MAHALANOBIS, P. C., *Sankyā*, 1935–6, **2**, 33.
43. TODD, J. R., Tea Res. Inst. E. Africa, Proc. 3rd Conference, 1955, Pamphlet No. 12, 23.
44. ROBERTS, E. A. H., *J. Sci. Fd and Agric.*, 1958, **9**, 381.
45. —— and SMITH, R. F., *Analyst*, 1961, **86**, 94.
46. LAMB, J., *Tea Quarterly*, 1935, **8**, 171.
47. Indian Tea Association, Scientific Dept. Annual Report, 1932, 77.
48. BOKUCHAVA, M. A., *et alii*, *C.R. Acad. Sci. U.S.S.R.*, 1954, **95**, 609. C. A., 1954, **48**, 8879.
49. BOKUCHAVA, M. A., and POPOV, V. R., ibid., 1954, **99**, 145. C. A., 1955, **49**, 3439.
50. ROBERTS, E. A. H., *Tea Quarterly*, 1961, **32**, 190.
51. WIGHT, W., and GILCHRIST, K. C. J. H., *Nature*, 1961, **191**, 14.

Chapter XIII

TEA MANUFACTURE

Withering—Rolling—Roll-breaking and Green-leaf Sifting—Fermentation—Firing—Grading and Sorting—Factory Hygiene—Factory Design and Organization—Current Innovations—Non-wither Teas—Green Tea—Tea Extracts.

ATTENTION has already been called to the fact that the fundamental process in black tea manufacture is that of enzymic fermentation of the catechin polyphenols. The train of different processes that fresh-plucked leaf undergoes is designed in the first place to prepare the leaf for this fermentation; in the second to establish the best conditions for its action and finally to arrest the process when it has gone far enough. Concomitant with the check to fermentation is the production of a dry easily handled product capable of more or less prolonged storage without deterioration.

The care and attention needed to ensure satisfactory manufacture should start in the field. The relationship between standard of plucking and the inherent quality of the leaf has already been dealt with: the treatment of the leaf from the moment of detachment from the bush to that at which manufacture proper begins is also of importance. The fermentation process begins immediately a leaf is bruised. If this occurs in the plucker's hand, or in the containers in which the leaf is transported to the factory, such fermentation is uncontrolled. Moreover bruised leaf dries out more quickly than undamaged leaf[1] and when stored or packed in bulk heats up, partly as a result of the exothermic nature of the fermentation reaction and partly as a result of continued respiration. These undesigned reactions are detrimental to the attainment of optimum conditions in subsequent processes. Careful handling of plucked leaf and avoidance of tight packing in bags, baskets or other containers are of the essence of good manufacturing technique.

WITHERING

In systems of traditional manufacture the first stage in the processing of tea is withering. Normally this is carried out by spreading thinly on banks of trays or "tats" made of tightly stretched jute

151

hessian or wire-netting. Ten to fifteen square feet per pound of fresh leaf is a normal density of spread. The tats are spaced five to six inches apart, to allow of free access of air, with alley-ways between each bank to allow of distribution and removal of leaf. In Assam the withering houses are usually detached from the rest of the factory and have no walls. In Ceylon and elsewhere they are an integral part of the building and form the upper storeys. These lofts have walls that are little more than a series of glazed windows that can be opened or shut as desired.

The open or "chung" type of withering accommodation admits of no control of rate of withering except by thickness of spread, and the length of the wither is dependent entirely on the prevailing hygrometric condition of the ambient air. This constitutes "natural withering" in its simplest form. In closed lofts natural withering can be carried out by opening the windows and, in addition, air movement can be provided by means of fans. Factories of this type are provided with central bulking chambers from which air drawn from outside is blown over the leaf throughout the length of the loft, from which it escapes at the far end by the adjustment of window apertures. When necessary during wet weather the relative humidity of the air is decreased by mixing with it in the bulking chamber a proportion of hot air from the driers. As an additional refinement, by means of other fans at the extremities of the lofts and by manipulation of the vents through which the air has access to the lofts, the airstream may be reversed. By these methods "artificial withering" is carried out and excessive gradients in the rate of withering can be avoided.

Some factories have "mobile tats." They are slung from pulleys travelling on overhead rails such that each individual bank of tats can be removed from its internal location and brought to a loading and weighing platform at any time. The lofts have no windows and withering is by forced draught, the air being conditioned or not at will. This system is economical of space since less alley-ways are necessary. The course of withering can be followed at intervals by automatic weighings of representative tats. Given a satisfactory standard of spreading, the control of withering is thereby considerably enhanced.

A recent innovation, or perhaps, more strictly, a renewal of a project of more than fifty years ago is drum withering. In place of withering tats, which demand a large amount of factory space, the leaf is withered in perforated revolving drums, capable of holding some fifteen hundred pounds of leaf, through which is blown hot air (*circa* 130° F.). Both space and time required to obtain the requisite degree of wither are reduced by this method.

51. Ceylon tea factory

52. Loading a mobile withering tat

53. Single-action
    tea roller

54. Double-action
    tea roller

55. Rolling room with battery of rollers

56. Withering drum

57. Green-leaf sifter

58. McKercher C.T.C. machine

The degree of wither regarded as satisfactory has been the subject of much investigation but no unanimity of opinion has been reached. This degree is commonly derived from the weight of the withered leaf expressed as a percentage of the weight of fresh leaf. The resultant value is frequently misleading because it does not take into account variability in the moisture content of the leaf or the presence of surface moisture. Since the object of withering is to produce from varying batches of leaf a residual material with a uniform moisture content, the only realistic check on percentage wither is the ratio of out-turn of dry tea to withered leaf. On the assumption that normal leaf without adherent moisture is used, the degree of wither aimed at in practice depends upon the type of tea to be produced and the method of manufacture. Light withers (40 to 42 per cent out-turn) are usual in Assam and East Africa, and medium to hard withers (45 to 50 per cent out-turn) are the norm in Ceylon. The average length of time for withering is eighteen to twenty hours when "tats" are used. There is much flexibility in this figure depending not only on the considerations aforementioned but on the dovetailing of one factory process with the ensuing ones. Drum withering can be accomplished in three hours.

The regulation of rates of withering obviously demands attention to the hygrometric condition of the air used. Keegel[2] gives close consideration to the principles involved and concludes that the basic requirements for an ideal wither are low wet-bulb temperatures, an ample supply of moving air and high hygrometric differences. The prime object in withering is to prepare the leaf for rolling by making the leaf tissues flaccid and permeable to the juices which the rolling will wring out and spread evenly upon the surface. This must not be allowed to obscure the fact that there are coincidental biochemical changes taking place which may affect ensuing processes. These changes raise two questions. Are they dependent on moisture loss in withering and do they affect the character of the finished tea?

The interim results from investigations now being made at the Tea Research Institute of Ceylon confirm and extend previous un-coordinated observations.[3, 4] After plucking enzyme activity and soluble amino-acid content increase for twenty hours: thereafter changes are erratic. Caffeine however increases throughout the experimental period (72 hours). These variations occur whether the leaf is withered or not. On the other hand, actual withering is neces-sary to bring about increasing permeability of the cell membranes on which, to a considerable degree, the mingling of enzyme, polyphenols and oxygen depends in orthodox manufacture. There is reasonable probability that these biochemical changes significantly influence the quality of the tea. Enhanced enzyme efficiency promotes quicker and more efficient fermentation; amino-acids are thought to influence colour and aroma. Caffeine is the stimulant that makes tea a desirable beverage.

The dissociation of chemical change from loss of water has a bearing on innovations in manufacture that will be described later in this chapter. Sanderson's[3, 4] theory of withering demands that there should be a pre-rolling stage for the promotion of chemical changes and then a thorough derangement of the cell contents. Orthodox manufacture provides both. Procedures which telescope the time interval associated with normal withering are not likely to benefit the quality of tea.

Insufficient attention to withering standards leads to many complications later. In the subsequent stage of rolling it is difficult to keep under-withered leaf from being thrown out of the machine, and in extreme instances the juices may be expressed and lost. When unduly wet the macerated leaf clogs the sieves of sifting machinery. Most serious of all, too light a wither will overtax the drier in the firing process. As regards effects on the character of the tea, under-withering tends to produce flaky tea of low apparent specific gravity. The cortex of the stalk is more easily removed during rolling when withers are too light, with a consequent increase in red leaf in the dried tea. Both these characteristics detract from the good appearance of tea. Long withers have a favourable effect on colour in the brewed tea but this is secured at the expense of quality. Where long withers are the result of too slow a removal of surface moisture there is risk of the rapid proliferation of ubiquitous and unwanted bacteria which produce dull and characterless teas.

ROLLING

When a satisfactory wither has been obtained the leaf is ready for rolling, which twists the leaf, breaks it up and expresses the juices. The machines used vary in size and design but their principles are alike: they compress and turn the leaf over, keeping it in continual motion, in a manner that is similar to, and derived from, the operation of rubbing leaf between the palms of the hand in primitive Chinese fashion. A typical roller consists of a circular table raised some three feet off the ground. Suspended above this is a smaller circular sleeve or box without top or bottom which under control of a revolving crank moves eccentrically over the surface of the table. In some designs the crank is double and the table also moves. Whether or not the movement is single or double action, the effect is the same, the cycle being characterized by the sum of the throws of the crank mechanism involved. The box has a slight clearance above the table and is fitted with a cap which can be raised or lowered within the confines of the box by means of a worm gear. The roller is set in motion and the box is charged with withered leaf. Pressure can be applied by lowering the cap on to the leaf. The pressure is maintained and regulated by spring compression. In this manner work is done on the leaf. The amount of work done depends on the cap pressure, the friction between the leaf and the container and the accompanying motion, which is governed by the speed and throw of the crank. There are various rolling régimes, some with and some without applied pressure. Rolling is usually carried out in spells of about half an hour for any one charge. Pressure is not usually applied continuously, the half-hour periods being divided into convenient subperiods of alternate application and release. At the end of the specified period the leaf is discharged through a door in the centre of the table.

Rolling is a repetitive operation and before outlining the entire procedure it will be convenient to consider what happens to the leaf during rolling. The circulation of the leaf in the roller and the shearing forces in play bruise and twist the leaf. This effect is accentuated by the presence on the roller table and the cap of a number of raised battens. Their type and number are various: some are no more than smoothly curved mouldings: others have angular cutting edges. In addition the table door may embody either a depression, or a rounded-off cone. These protuberances increase the friction and the shearing forces and increase the work done on the leaf, though at the same time they diminish its circulation. Under high pressure with severe battens the leaf tends to disintegrate early. Without pressure the action is more directed towards wringing and twisting the leaf.

During rolling the juices are expressed from the leaves and spread as a thin film on their surface. This juice expression is not dependent entirely on leaf tearing and abrasion. The physical condition of the cell tissues after withering is such that the liquids are forced out without actual rupture of the cells. It apparently needs little deformity of the protoplasm of the tissues to break down the division between the contents of the vacuoles and the plastids, and in fact this can be performed by means other than that of doing work on the leaf.[6] The net result is that the catechins and enzyme, originally separated in the leaf, are thoroughly mixed and that both are exposed to the atmosphere. Thus, as mentioned in the chapter on the chemistry of the leaf, the three appropriate constituents necessary for fermentation are brought together and the enzymic oxidation of the catechin polyphenols begins. The green colour diminishes and the brown or coppery colour of the oxidation products begins to appear.

At this stage there are a number of points related to the design of rollers and to procedure that require emphasis because they affect the whole course of manufacture and the quality of finished tea. The first is that the onset of rolling is accompanied by the evolution of heat. In part this is mechanical heat generated by the frictional forces, but a significant amount is due to the exothermic nature of the chemical action of oxidation. The resultant rise in temperature of the leaf mass accelerates fermentation but heating must not be allowed to proceed to excess. Opinions differ as to the allowable optimum but it is between the range of 80–90° F.[2]

Pressure, by consolidating the leaf, confines the accumulated heat and that is why, in traditional rolling programmes, periods with and without pressure are generally alternated. Pressure and battens impede the circulation of leaf and prevent the constant air interchange within the mass. Thus, too high a pressure may have two kinds of deleterious action: temperature may become excessive and insufficient oxygen may come into contact with the expressed juices. Both have undesirable effects on quality.

Excessive pressure in the early stages of rolling affects the physical appearance of the tea. Well-twisted leaf is desired by the tea trade and this can only be secured if the twist is imparted before the leaf laminae begin to disintegrate. Particles of tea that will pass a sieve with five meshes to the inch are incapable of retaining the twist and consequently excessive breaking up of leaf at an early stage gives rise to a flaky tea.[2] Moreover, hard rolling at an early stage tends to strip the cortex from the stalk, particularly if leaf is under-withered, and produces the red leaf referred to in the previous section.

At the end of the first stage of rolling the tenderer portions of the leaf have been detached and these are separated from the bulk by discharging the roller and mechanically sifting the contents. More detailed consideration of the green-leaf sifting will be given in the ensuing section. The leaf which passes the sieves is removed and set up, as subsequently described, to continue its fermentation: that which passes over the mesh is recharged into a roller and the second-stage rolling is started.

The number of times a batch of leaf is rolled varies according to the type of tea to be produced, the degree of wither of the leaf and the kind of roller used. In general the lightly withered leaf common to Assam and African procedures receives a smaller number of rolls than medium or hard withered leaf in Ceylon. The usual range is from three to five rolling periods. The aim is first to twist the leaf and then progressively to break it up into small particles by increased pressure till the major portion has been sifted through the green leaf sifters. Finally there is left an unreduced bulk of larger and tougher fragments commonly referred to as "big bulk." The Ceylon criterion for well rolled tea is that big bulk should not exceed 10 per cent of the total charge, but in Assam and Africa much greater percentages are usual.[2] At the end of a complete series of rolling and sifting operations the undifferentiated mass of leaf charged into the roller has been divided into a series of portions variously termed "dhools," "mahls" or "fines," one for each roll, plus the residual big bulk.

ROLL-BREAKING AND GREEN-LEAF SIFTING

On discharge from the roller the leaf mass is more or less compressed into lumps. These are broken up in the sifting process by the machine which usually combines the operation of roll-breaker and sifter. In essence this is a rectangular sieve, set at a moderate angle, mechanically agitated. The roller discharge is fed into a hopper in which beaters revolve to break up the mass, after which the tea falls onto the sieve and slowly travels to the other end for discharge. In the course of this passage the smaller particles fall through.

The roll-breaker and green-leaf sifter performs three essential functions. In the first instance it cools the leaf and thus prevents the retention of excessive heat: secondly, it aerates the mass, and thirdly, by sieving out particles of small size, it separates leaf into portions that will be reasonably uniform in their rate of fermentation. To achieve this uniformity careful operation is needed. The leaf should be fed continuously at an even rate and be well spread across the width of the sieve. The angle of tilt of the machine should be so gauged that the passage along it is neither too rapid nor too slow. Rate of feeding should be regulated so that the layer on the sieves is not too thick to impede the fall through. Leaf should never be brushed through the sieve as this leads to dhools lacking even the semblance of uniformity. Since the large particles tend to accumulate at the lower end it is common to have two sizes of mesh in the frame, the smaller mesh at the lower end. The mesh apertures used vary but the norm is five to the inch.[2] The percentage that passes the sieve is regulated by various considerations apart from the size of hole. Some sieves have thicker wire than others and some are made from punched metal sheet. Accordingly size and number of holes vary according to the design of the machine. The smaller meshes turn out teas with superior liquors, other things being equal.

When the charge from the rollers has thus been differentiated into dhools it is possible to form an opinion of what has been happening during rolling, and to gauge whether the régime has been too severe or not severe enough. In general, early dhools should be proportionally smaller than the mid-period ones, but dhool percentages are not a final criterion of good rolling: evenness of dhool is equally important. Nevertheless, if, under a standard working régime, day-to-day dhool percentages vary grossly there is compelling reason to investigate the uniformity of wither, the application of pressure in the rollers and the technique of feeding the sifters.

FERMENTATION

Fermentation starts in the rollers but is continued in the dhool stage. The sifted dhools are spread out in thin layers, in order to continue the oxidative processes. There is great variety in the materials that are used to accommodate this spread-out leaf. Tiles, cement and aluminium are most commonly used, the essential point being that they should be easily cleaned. The thickness of spread controls three important factors, the temperature of the leaf, the rate of moisture loss and the access of oxygen. With layers two inches thick temperature losses sufficient to retard fermentation are not likely. Some factories install air-conditioning plant to ensure controlled conditions. Good air circulation without draughts is needed to attain good fermentation conditions. In hot climates the air is kept humid with less than 4° F. hygrometric difference. In colder regions the circulating atmosphere is artificially heated. In either event moist air, to prevent surface drying, is advisable. For economical working it is better to ferment in a special fermentation room whose atmospheric conditions can be easily controlled.

During fermentation the leaf changes colour and becomes a dark copper colour. The typical aroma develops and by the subjective judgement of its intensity the period necessary for completion is judged. Time of fermentation is reckoned from the time at which rolling begins and it should be as short as is practicable. After four and a half hours there is appreciable loss of quality.[2] If dhools retain their green colour on the fermenting trays, the indications are that the rolling has not been sufficient either in severity or in duration. The fault cannot be rectified by longer fermentation which only leads to dull teas. As fermentation progresses the soluble content capable of extraction in the brew decreases. Over-fermented teas accordingly lose strength even though they appear to increase in colour.

Daily washing of fermentation surfaces is indispensable. Particularly with soft withered teas they tend to become covered with a layer of fermented juices which is a favourable medium for bacterial growth. When fermentation is judged to be sufficient the dhools are transferred to the drier but not usually in the order in which they have been produced.

Because of the heat generated in the rollers the later dhools have undergone fermentation for a longer period at a higher and, if properly controlled, more favourable temperature than the dhools exposed early in the process on the fermenting trays at room temperature. Later dhools therefore require less time on the fermentation racks and are ready for firing first. Whilst the firing operation is taking place on later dhools the earlier batches are completing theirs. The aim should therefore be to co-ordinate rolling periods, fermentation intervals and firing sequence so as to make allowances for varying rates of fermentation and avoid extremes in fermentation times.[2] Satisfactory schedules are more easily constructed when the roller-charging intervals are short, always provided that they are not so curtailed as to make the work done on the leaf ineffectual in releasing the juice. Retention of flavour is favoured by reasonably short charging intervals.

FIRING

Medium withered leaf has an out-turn value of 45 per cent, and consequently during the firing or drying process moisture, equivalent to about half the weight of the dhool, has to be evaporated (allowance being made for small losses during the manufacturing processes of rolling, roll-breaking and fermentation).

The general principle adopted in firing is that of subjecting the fermented tea to a forced blast of hot air in such a manner that the hottest air comes first into contact with the driest tea. To bring this about the older driers, some of which are still in use, were provided with a banked series of perforated trays carrying the dhools, which were systematically altered in position as the drying operation proceeded; a fresh tray being inserted at the exhaust end as the trays were moved and the final one removed. A similar pattern of movement was also provided for in machines which had fixed trays built in narrow strips which could be mechanically tilted so as to discharge their leaf onto the tray below, leaving the upper one ready to load with the next portion of unfired dhool. Modern machines employ the principle of perforated sections mounted on an endless chain. The sections are arranged in a tier of six units which alternate in their direction of motion. The tea is fed onto the top section, and moves in conveyor-belt fashion till it discharges onto the tray immediately below, which is moving in the opposite direction; and so on till the dried tea is discharged at the bottom. Hot air is provided by means of a furnace or steam boiler through which pass tubes connecting with the outer atmosphere. An induced draught is maintained by fans. The dhools are fed into a hopper ancillary to which is an automatic spreader. Thickness of spread, speed of trays and volume

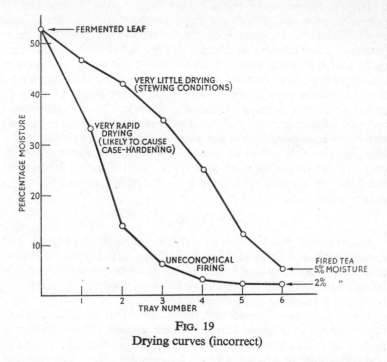

FIG. 19
Drying curves (incorrect)

of air blown through can all be regulated at will. Automatic recording thermometers register both inlet and outlet temperatures. Inlet temperatures usually range from 180° F. to 200° F., according to the degree of wither, and outlet temperatures are in the range of 120° F. to 130° F.[2, 7]

Some modern installations in which the furnace fuel is oil dispense with air heating tubes and blow the products of combustion, diluted with the appropriate quantity of fresh air, directly over the tea. Thermodynamic efficiency is increased by as much as 25 per cent by this means and with perfect combustion no taint is imparted to the tea. The products of combustion contain a detectable amount of sulphur dioxide. In order to prevent its corrosive effect on the drier

59. Tea drier *in situ*

60. Stove for tea drier *in situ*

61. Tea drier with stove

62. Tea cutting and sifting

63. Tea sifter

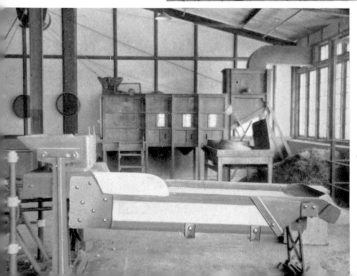

64. Tea sifter and winnower (in background

mechanism exhaust temperatures must be maintained at 140° F. when this type of direct firing is used.

In a properly regulated drier the estimated evaporation constant is 0·75 lb water per 1,000 cubic feet of air, at the intake and exhaust temperatures previously recorded. There should be a regular increase of dry-bulb temperature as the tea moves down the drying chamber

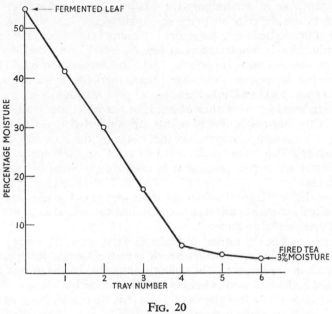

FIG. 20
Drying curve (correct)

and a corresponding regular decrease in moisture content from tray to tray. The wet-bulb temperature should remain constant at about 100° F.[8] The critical temperature to watch is that of the exhaust. If this temperature is too low the moisture content of the finished tea will be excessive: if too high, the drying process will be inefficient in the sense that hot air will be wasted. Low exhaust temperatures tend to give drying curves (constructed by plotting moisture contents against tray sequence) that are convex to the tray ordinate and indicate ineffective drying in the early stages. On the other hand when drying curves are concave the rapid drying in the initial stages is apt to case-harden teas and prevent even drying throughout the particles. These possibilities call for meticulous care in regulation of spread, tray speed and air flow. The easiest method of adjustment is by altering the air flow. At the temperatures recorded, efficient drying to a moisture content of 3 per cent can be effected in about twenty minutes with modern machines.

During the drying process the enzyme responsible for fermentation is inactivated. After the tea is dry maturation processes occur but these are not due to enzyme activity. The manner of firing plays an important role in determining the quality. Teas fired at high temperatures are deficient in pungency, quality and flavour, but their keeping properties are satisfactory.[9] Contrariwise teas can be satisfactorily fired at temperatures as low as 160° F. provided that the final moisture content is correct. These teas retain their quality and flavour but deteriorate on storage. Tea is markedly hygroscopic and if left exposed will pick up as much as 13 per cent additional moisture and turn mouldy. Teas thus affected, or tea which has been underfired in the normal course of events, are subjected to an additional firing at lower temperatures than that of the original operation. This "final firing" has no beneficial effect on quality since it merely checks deterioration: its sole purpose is to improve the keeping properties of the tea.

After delivery from the drier the tea is spread out to cool and then temporarily stored to await sorting. Retention of heat in newly fired tea is detrimental to quality.

Fired tea has the typical appearance familiar to all users of the beverage. When manufactured with care the twisted leaf particles are black in appearance. The colour is imparted by the dried film of oxidized and condensed catechins spread over the leaf tissues. Closer examination with a lens shows that this film, despite its black appearance in bulk, is really a translucent treacle-brown colour. Teas that have been improperly made, with too much maceration of leaf in the process, are browner. Black tea itself, if crushed, becomes a dull-brown powder. Despite the separation of particles by sifting during the rolling programme, the particles of the dried dhools are heterogeneous to a considerable degree and are brought to a greater state of uniformity by grading or sorting in the dry state.

GRADING AND SORTING

Grading is carried out for the most part on mechanically oscillated sieves, similar in general principle to those used in the green stage, and fitted with meshes of appropriate size. In some machines the sieves are in banks of diminishing mesh size such that the outfall of the upper member falls on to the lower. In contradistinction to green-leaf sifting, it is the tea that remains on the sieve which is the objective.

The products of the various sifting operations constitute the different grades, and are defined by the meshes of two sieves through the larger of which the particles pass, and on the smaller of which they are retained. The grades in general production are named as follows: Broken Orange Pekoe; Broken Pekoe; Orange Pekoe; Pekoe; Souchong; Broken Orange Pekoe Fannings; Fannings and Dust. The grade specification is entirely artificial, though not completely arbitrary. The broken grades and the B.O.P. fannings should have substantial contributions from the early dhools: the leaf grades come mainly from the later ones. There is thus an approximate division in type between grades made up of the tenderer portions of the leaf and those from the tougher and more mature portions of the flush. Broken Orange Pekoe at its best should contain a high proportion of buds (tip): Orange Pekoe is characterized by the abundance of twisted tender stalk. The Pekoe and Souchong grades are more compact and dense. During recent years the emphasis has been on the production of small teas, and to produce these a considerable amount of cutting has been resorted to. Consequently the tendency is for later dhools to contribute substantially to the Broken Pekoe grade and to increase the proportion of broken grades turned out. This has emphasized more acutely the entirely artificial standards of grading. Excessive cutting or sifting of tea to ensure uniform grades tends to rub off the film of fermentation products, previously mentioned, and imparts a grey colour to the particles, which is undesirable. Faulty rolling and uneven dhools are the underlying reasons for the need to cut and over-sift tea.

The sieve standards adopted for regulating grades differ in the various countries and even in different districts in the same country. Keegel[2] defines a true Ceylon B.O.P. as passing a No. 10 sieve but not a No. 18: Harler,[8] following the Indian tradition, specifies the combination of No. 8 and No. 10. Notwithstanding local variation in the sizes of sieves that are used, the different grades are recognizable by their appearance, and a good deal of judgement is necessary in deciding the detailed procedure for the production of a particular grade.

Winnowing in some form or other is a routine practice, and, according to the size and density of the particles, separates fannings and dust, and carries away the fibrous residue tea-fluff which is of no commercial value as a grade. All grades contain a certain amount of atypical particles, particularly pieces of tough stalk. The better the technique of plucking and manufacture the less evident this material should be. It is removed by hand-picking or by means of a special type of sieve whose holes, being raised on nipples, allow the passage of the lighter particles whilst the stalk remains in the hollows between the nipples.

The exposure to the atmosphere of particles of tea thinly spread on sieve trays offers ideal conditions for the uptake of moisture. Teas perfectly dried can increase in moisture content beyond the danger point of 5 to 6 per cent during sorting, if the humidity of the atmosphere is not controlled. Air with a relative humidity of 60 to 65 per cent is in hygroscopic equilibrium with tea, and if sorting-rooms are kept at this humidity tea will neither pick up nor lose moisture.[10, 11] It is of the essence of good manufacture that teas should be sorted daily and not left exposed to the air. Finished grades are stored in air-tight bins till a sufficient quantity has accumulated to pack a consignment or "break". The size of the break is a matter of convenience provided that no grade consists of less than six chests, which is the smallest lot allowable in a tea auction.

Before tea is packed the accumulated series of daily batches of each grade are bulked and mixed in order to ensure as high a degree of uniformity as possible. The tea is then packed into chests holding approximately 100 lb. or 50 lb. (half chests). These chests are usually of plywood lined with aluminium foil and paper and sealed with similar material.

FACTORY HYGIENE

At all stages of manufacture the maintenance of hygienic conditions is of paramount importance not only in relation to accepted standards imposed by food regulations but in order to turn out good quality tea. Tea is very liable to pick up taints, and when they occur the cause is frequently faulty handling of the tea itself or of the machinery used.

Hygienic precautions should start in the field, the fundamental maxim being that there, and in all subsequent operations, leaf should be kept off the ground. Baskets, sacks, withering tats and sieves should be kept in good repair so that foreign substances do not become mixed with the leaf. Before charging rollers it is advisable to run leaf over a coarse sifter to eliminate fragments of earth, stone, baskets or hessian that may be present. This has the additional advantage of getting rid of a good deal of dried-out leaf fragments that are unfit for manufacture. All machinery used in the green-leaf stage needs daily washing and scouring, particularly if the leaf is soft withered. Accumulated juice on fermenting trays, in the mesh of green-leaf sifters and in batten crevices or rollers, will putrefy if not removed, and, at the least will favour bacterial infection, and at the worst lead to taints. In Assam and elsewhere it has been found advantageous to flame these surfaces with a painter's blowlamp. There is always a certain amount of spill from rollers and roll-breakers. This should never be returned to the bulk. The quantity can be reduced to small proportions by careful handling and should be discarded. Small pieces of metal are apt to wear off the moving parts of machines. They are predominatingly of iron and steel and can be collected by feeding tea into the chests through a magnetic extractor. Strict personal hygiene amongst all workers should be insisted on. Ample washing facilities and the issue of frequently laundered protective clothing are very necessary. Tea sifting necessarily produces a considerable amount of tea dust which is detrimental to the working personnel, the tea and the machinery. Every factory needs efficient dust extraction fans to minimize this nuisance.

FACTORY DESIGN AND ORGANIZATION

Tea factories are functional in design and, though there are differences in the detail of both plan and construction, the general run of modern factories conform to a recognized type. What may be called the Ceylon type, with self-contained withering accommodation, is well distributed through Ceylon, South India, Africa and Indonesia, and consequently a description of its more important features will serve to illustrate the nature of a typical layout.

The ground floor, built of stone or brick, houses the necessary machinery: the superstructure of withering lofts is carried on a steel framework and is clad with corrugated-iron sheets. These lofts are divided into three sections, comprising a centre air bulking-chamber that runs the entire height of the building, flanked on either side by paired wings, storey by storey. Vents connect the bulking chamber with the ground floor and with each loft. Propeller fans in the outside walls of the bulking chamber provide for air distribution throughout the system, either direct from the exterior atmosphere, or from this and the hot air discharged by driers in the ground floor. By means of stairs and hoists there is direct access to withering lofts from the factory compound. The floor of the loft above the rolling equipment is usually provided with chutes for the delivery of withered leaf direct to the rollers.

The ground floor is divided into separate chambers assigned to the respective processes of rolling and roll-breaking, fermentation, firing and sorting and packing. In modern factories the stove units for driers are contained in a completely separate chamber, and by so doing fire risks are minimized and cleanliness is maintained. The arrangement of rooms is ordered by the progression of operations in manufacture so that the tea passes from rolling room to the fermentation chamber, on to the driers and out to the sifting room with a minimum of transportation from one unit of the factory to another. Rollers are commonly disposed along the outside walls of the rolling room leaving the central portion for roll-breakers which can serve either rank of rollers. The party-wall between firing and sifting rooms is occupied by storage bins accessible from either room. In a fully equipped factory, in addition to the power house, there is usually a chamber adjacent to the rolling and fermenting rooms equipped with humidifying apparatus (Fig. 21).

In general character tea manufacture is a batch process though attempts to make it continuous are receiving attention. But whether or not these projects prove practicable there remains the task of ordering the succession of different processes in such a way that there will be no significant halts or bottlenecks in the processes. The uneven incidence of crop from season to season, and to a less extent from day to day, calls for careful decision of the number and size of units of machinery at every stage of the process. Otherwise at rush periods machinery will be overtaxed and bottlenecks produced, whilst in off-seasons much expensive machinery will lie idle.

In planning the daily routine of manufacture drying is the crucial factor, and all calculations regarding batch quantities are dependent on drier capacity. Once a drier is brought into operation there should, as far as possible, be no gaps in firing till the last lot is discharged. If long gaps occur fuel and heat are wasted and the working temperatures are disturbed. From this basic factor of drier capacity all else proceeds. A sound manufacturing programme demands a detailed knowledge of what percentage dhools will be aimed at, their period of fermentation, the intervals of charging rollers and the gross quantity of leaf taken in a batch. This in turn will affect the number and size of the roller combinations used. It is not only the economics of the operations that are of importance: the quality of the tea is vitally affected according as processes are curtailed or over-extended because of inefficient integration in devising a workable programme involving half a dozen disparate processes. Whitehead[12] and Keegel[2] have made great improvements in factory organization by considering all these factors and working out a harmoniously progressive scheme to suit different styles of manufacture and a variety of equipment. These schemes which can be symbolically posted up in factory premises have the unique advantage that they facilitate supervision. When used, they show the executive in charge what every piece of

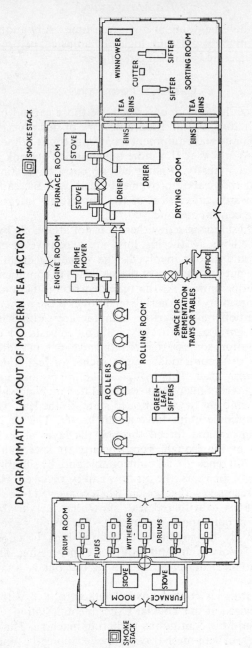

FIG. 21

DIAGRAMMATIC LAY-OUT OF MODERN TEA FACTORY

machinery should be doing at any given time. Any anomaly can be immediately investigated and logically adjusted before the whole train of manufacture is thrown out of gear.

CURRENT INNOVATIONS

The processes heretofore described are those carried out in traditional manufacture. Within the framework of this procedure, refinements in technique and equipment have from time to time been introduced. Since World War II a more adventurous outlook has characterized the tea industry. Rising labour costs have stimulated the search for mechanical improvements that will increase efficiency and move towards conversion of the imperfectly integrated batch-process into a continuous one.

Efficient and standardized withering is not attainable by any of the traditional methods. Withering lofts are expensive in capital cost, maintenance and labour involved. The withering drum provides a compact unit, but the bruising of the leaf leads to complications in the subsequent fermentation. At the time of writing, the most powerful contender for priority in withering techniques is the withering trough. The equipment offered by various manufacturers differs in detail but the overall design is standard. A typical unit consists of a trough with a wire-mesh bottom some 50 ft. in length and 5–6 ft. in width with sides deep enough to accommodate eight inches of leaf, that is, about 1,500 lb. of fresh flush. This trough is the uppermost portion of an air flue with a rectangular cross-section 4 ft. 6 in. high which conveys the air, in its ambient or conditioned state, to the leaf. The troughs, singly or in multiple units, have an air heater. The air is propelled by a powerful fan and forced through the layer of leaf along the whole length of the trough. Temperature, air speed and resultant hygrometric difference are all controllable and, by suitable structural arrangements of air vents, the air flow can be reversed. Harler[8] gives figures for percentage wither which, when converted into the out-turn ratio of made tea to withered leaf, show that the variability of the sampled leaf is only about 2 per cent. The troughs are frequently supplemented by air-conditioned storage bins to cope with the exigencies of factory hours and sequence of processing. Trough withering is economical in space and in labour but is a conventional batch-process.

As a step towards continuous manufacture, two withering units have been devised at the Tocklai Experimental Station:[5, 8] the withering tunnel and the continuous withering machine. The former has stacked trolleys of wire-mesh trays propelled along the tunnel through which conditioned air is blown. Rapid withers of $2\frac{1}{2}$ to 4 hours' duration can be effected.

In the continuous withering machine, the leaf trays traverse the whole 18 ft. length of the totally enclosed chamber thirty-one times, starting at the bottom and being elevated traverse by traverse. When at the end of 170 minutes they emerge at the top, each tray has travelled 560 ft. under the influence of conditioned air entering at one end and being discharged at the other. These machines are designed to be used in conjunction with continuous rolling equipment as indicated below.

The fundamental process in the manufacture of all black tea is the abrasion of the leaf to ensure the intimate reaction of catechin, enzyme and oxygen. Straightforward maceration of the leaf would be the simplest and most efficient method of doing this but such a course has various disadvantages. The more efficient the process the flakier the teas and the trade does not like flaky teas. With light withers (or no wither at all) there is the risk of losing large volumes of juice which have to be returned to the leaf with not very satisfactory effects on subsequent processes. Nevertheless, for a good many years, the pattern of grading has been altering in the direction of smaller teas. Mechanical packaging has had a marked influence on this change. Consequently, where strength and colour are the most desirable and in some instances the only attainable characteristics, there is a movement away from traditional rolling techniques into methods that mince the leaf, with striking effects on the aforementioned attributes. It is reported that in the Assam valley 80 per cent of the tea is manufactured by such methods, and in Africa the same trend is accelerating. [13]

As previously mentioned, the design of orthodox rollers has been changed. Before systematic research on tea manufacture was carried out the accent, as far as rolling was concerned, was on pressure applied by the roller cap. The deficiencies of this emphasis were revealed when rolling was considered in terms of work done, as indicated by power consumption records in kilowatt-hours on electrically driven rollers. Lamb's extensive studies showed that the greater part of the work done in a conventional roller is done near the centre. Dispensing with pressure caps and battens, he experimented with central fittings of various shapes which were effective in varying degrees and did not impede the free motion of the leaf, as caps and battens do. There is a diminution of work on the leaf as rolling proceeds, and there is no way of compensating for this except by a change of fitting. This inflexibility has militated against widespread adoption of this type of equipment. The working compromise that has emerged is the Keegel cone, a simple 45° cone rounded at the top, installed centrally on a flat table with few battens, and surmounted by a battenless pressure cap.

Returning to the subject of unconventional equipment, there are three machines which are in common use and replace or supplement orthodox rollers. The Legg cutter is in origin a tobacco cutter. The leaf, propelled under pressure through a narrow aperture, is shredded into strips whose fineness is adjustable. It is sometimes used on unwithered leaf and, especially if cuts are repeated on the same leaf, gives rise to loss of juice. The shreds can be rolled in an orthodox fashion to give a semblance of twist.

The McKercher C.T.C. with its crushing, tearing and curling action has stainless steel cylindrical rollers which revolve at differential rates and through which the leaf passes. The roller surfaces are not smooth as in the Clivemeare machine but are ridged superficially and macerate the withered leaf very efficiently. Two successive passages through the machine are commonly given and, with or without roll breaking, the leaf is ready for the fermenting table. Preparatory to being treated in the C.T.C. machine, the leaf may be rolled once in an orthodox roller or passed through a Rotorvane.

The Rotorvane, one of a number of machines of new design associated with the name of I. McTear of the Tocklai Station's Engineering Department, is in effect an elaborate disintegrator.[5] The rotor shaft, armed with vanes, propels the leaf towards the exit against the resistance of fixed counter-vanes projecting from the casing. Pressure is built up at the exit by a hinged door capable of adjustment. A unit of one Rotorvane and two C.T.C. machines with different roller settings, all linked by conveyor belts, provides a significant advance towards the goal of automation in tea manufacture. The use of these machines has cut down drastically the duration of rolling. The thorough maceration of the leaf makes fermentation quicker. The shortness of the process ensures that all the leaf starts fermenting at the same time and the risk of bacterial contamination is lessened. The teas are not so black as orthodox teas and they are unmistakably flaky.

In orthodox manufacture the well-appreciated characteristics of good appearance are a helpful indication of careful manufacture, but when the whole nature of an operation is changed these criteria are no longer relevant. The brisk, strong and coloury liquors that these machines produce are unmistakable.

It is probable that in India and Africa the new methods will oust the old as equipment is renewed. In Ceylon the issue is doubtful. The fact that striving for colour in high-grown teas leads to loss of quality is well authenticated but it is not altogether improbable that a satisfactory technique for high-grown tea may be worked out. Times and opinions change and it must not be forgotten that thirty years ago, when the original C.T.C. machine was launched, it had a mixed reception and only a limited success.

To complete the description of new equipment designed for automation mention must be made of further innovations introduced by the Tocklai Station. A fermenting tunnel which can take the discharge from a roller of the C.T.C. type is totally enclosed and as the fermenting trays move along it has oxygen fed to it in predetermined volumes. From the fermenting machine the dhools move to a Continuous Tray tea drier.[5] In this machine the trays retain the dhool throughout the drying process without any discharge from one to another as they progress along the drying chamber. As a result the risks of uneven distribution are substantially reduced.

NON-WITHER TEAS

The manufacture of tea without a preliminary withering process has obvious attractions and has been commercially carried out on a small scale. The elimination of withering makes necessary a change in rolling technique, for orthodox rollers cannot cope with unwithered leaf which is flung out of them in every direction. Recourse is therefore had to rollers of the type described in the foregoing section. Teas thus produced have the recognizable advantages of all teas processed by these machines, strength, good colour and bright and uniform infusions, but they have countervailing defects. Without withering there is no way of getting rid of superficial moisture and consequently difficulties arise in the firing process. Their flakiness is more extreme than that of teas produced by the same machines from withered leaf. Though fermentation is rapid, which is advantageous, it is not complete: the wetness of the dhool militates against oxygen penetration and, in the cup, a good deal of unfermented catechin flavours the liquor, giving it a bitter or brassy taste. It is possible that the absence of the postulated chemical wither is a contributory cause of this undesirable characteristic. Prior leaf storage might improve the finished product. In small quantities the market can use these teas and the writer has had experience of improvement in valuation, backed by corresponding increase in market price, when a small percentage of witherless leaf was incorporated with orthodox leaf before rolling. Such small additions create no rolling problem.

GREEN TEA

The world tea trade is concerned almost entirely with the manufacture of black tea made according to the procedures outlined in this chapter. Certain local markets such as North Africa require green tea. In China and Japan it is manufactured in considerable amounts.

Green tea is an entirely different type of commodity from black tea, inasmuch as its preparation depends on killing the enzyme that is responsible for the typical fermentation of catechins. This is done either by steaming the leaf for a few minutes in perforated drums supplied with a steam blast, or by rapid and partial drying in hot pans. As there are no fermentation products, except those incidental to leaf damage before steaming, the leaf remains green. There is no typical tea aroma developed and when infused the liquors are pale primrose coloured. To the hardened drinker of black tea the brew is insipid and slightly bitter.

TEA EXTRACTS

Coffee extracts have been produced for so long and have been commercially so successful that it is not surprising that efforts have been made to produce a palatable tea extract that can be reduced to powder form. Tea producers would benefit materially if a concentrate that was acceptable could be shipped from the growing region instead of the crude bulk of tea.

Efforts to manufacture and market a concentrate have not yet reached noticeable success. There is little information available of what sort of process is suitable and effective from patent literature. The known variations in technique appear to cover direct extraction from black tea, and extraction from fermented leaf with or without supplementary oxidation by chemical agents.

REFERENCES

1. LAMB, J., *Tea Quarterly*, 1949, **20**, 24.
2. KEEGEL, E. L., *Tea Manufacture in Ceylon*, 2nd edn. 1958, Tea Res. Inst. Ceylon, Monograph No. 4.
3. SANDERSON, G. W., *Tea Quarterly*, 1964, **35**, 146.
4. ——, *J. Sci. Fd Agric.*, 1964, **15**, 634.
5. Tocklai Experimental Station Reports, 1957–62.
6. CHILD, R., Tea Res. Inst. E. Africa., Proc. 2nd Conference, 1954, Pamphlet No. 8, 9.
7. LAMB, J., *Tea Quarterly*, 1942, **15**, 5, 13.

8. HARLER, C. R., *The Culture and Marketing of Tea*, 3rd edn., O.U.P., 1964.
9. LAMB, J., *Tea Quarterly*, 1939, **12**, 171; 1940, **13**, 156.
10. PETCH, T., ibid., 1928, **1**, 24.
11. LAMB, J., ibid., 1935, **8**, 171.
12. ELLIOT, E. C. and WHITEHEAD, F. J., *Tea Planting in Ceylon*, 1930, Times of Ceylon, Colombo.
13. SANDERSON, G. W., *Tea Quarterly*, 1963, **54**, 179.

Chapter XIV

THE TEA TRADE AND INDUSTRY

*Tea Sales—Blending—Tea Tasting—Tea Tasting Terms
—Standards of Purity—The Tea Regulation Scheme—Tea
Market Expansion—Miscellaneous Organizations—Tea Re-
search.*

THE tea industry does not produce a uniform product. The characteristics of an accepted grade such as Broken Orange Pekoe vary to
some extent from country to country, district to district and from
estate to estate. Superimposed on these broad differences are others
determined by the season of the year during which the leaf is harvested
and manufactured. The tea buyer takes all these factors into consideration. From long experience he knows the type of tea to be
expected at any particular time from a particular locality, and even
from a particular estate, and in his operations his interest is centred
on the individual estate or group of estates. When he buys, he is not
buying in bulk but in a series of small lots some of which may be no
greater than 600 lb. Consequently, bearing in mind the multiplicity
of estates, it will be readily appreciated that the marketing of tea is
a very intricate business.[1]

TEA SALES

Tea may be sold by private treaty and on forward contracts either
in the countries of origin or of consumption, or on the water but the
vast majority of sales are effected in the established tea markets of
the world by public auction. The traditional markets are London,
Amsterdam, Calcutta and Colombo. National independence has
altered the pattern of these markets: more teas are sold in local
markets than heretofore and new markets have been established in
Cochin, Chittagong, Nairobi and Jakarta. The sales procedure varies
somewhat in the different markets but London may be regarded as
typical. To complete the account of what happens to tea in its course
from the field to consumer, this chapter will describe the handling of
tea on the London market and will then pass on to consider other
aspects of the trade inherent in the conduct of the industry.

Ordinarily, an invoice of tea, made up of the accepted grades, is shipped by the producers' agents in the country of origin to the corresponding agents in London, accompanied by all relevant documents relating to its origin, grades, weight and packing. On reception it is stored in a warehouse where every chest is checked for alteration in weight during transit and sampled by an augur specially designed for the purpose. These operations substantiate the details given in the documents. They also provide an opportunity for Customs officials to examine the teas under the provisions of the Customs and Excise Act 1952, to which reference will be made later.

A Central Sampling Depot acting for both buying- and selling-brokers makes up samples from the "show package" for distribution to brokers and prospective buyers prior to the forthcoming auction. These samples are reported on by the respective tea-tasters and thus each party in the transaction has an opportunity to value each lot. In the meantime the selling-broker acting for the producer prepares his catalogue for the sale showing the warehouse location of the tea, the estate name, the number of chests and total weight of each grade, and the weight of the standard unit of six chests. On the basis of this information the selling-brokers solicit tentative orders for the teas in the forthcoming auction.

The London Tea Auctions, which have been held since 1834, take place in the public Auction Room at Plantation House, Mincing Lane, on the first three days of each week. The conduct of the Auctions is arranged by the Tea Brokers Association, whose Conditions of Sale, as printed in each selling-brokers' catalogue, are binding on all sections of the Trade: these conditions of sale were originally agreed between producers, buyers and brokers. Each selling-broker sells his own teas, starting the auction at a figure near to his own valuation, and the lowest increment is a bid of one farthing per pound. The bids are made by buying-brokers acting on behalf of their customers, and thus the buyer of a tea remains anonymous at the time of the sale. When a sale is completed the buying-broker is under obligation, if requested, to reveal his principal within twenty-four hours, and, having paid a deposit on the purchase is allowed ninety days to complete the transaction. Usually delivery is taken within a few days.

The flow of tea from the producing countries is irregular in volume owing to seasonal variation in crop which in turn is controlled by climate. This is specially true of North Indian teas which are all produced within a consecutive period of six to eight months each year. It is therefore necessary at certain times of the year for the Regulation of Sales Joint Committee to regulate weekly offerings within the physical limits of a day's auction. Sixty to eighty thousand chests are considered a reasonable quantity to handle each week. Without this regulation the disposal of tea during some periods of the year would become chaotic, and the stability of the market would be affected by either surfeit or shortage.

BLENDING

The grades into which tea is sorted in producer's factories are not sold as such to consumers. Retail tea, whether sold loose, or, more usually, in the branded packet, is invariably a blend of different grades derived from a variety of estates, and usually from more than a single country of origin. The blend may contain in various proportions twenty to forty different components.

There are several important factors to be considered in making up a blend. The blend in a branded packet must remain constant in type but it would not be possible for it to be compounded from the same ingredients month in, month out. Typical reasons for this are the seasonal changes in quality and the fact that different regions produce their high-quality teas at different times. For example, in Assam the "second flush" teas produced between April and June and the "autumnals" at the end of the growing season have a better reputation than the early or the rainy season teas. In Ceylon with diverse climatic conditions in the eastern and western districts there are two quality seasons, June to September in the former and December to February in the latter. The blender must therefore vary his quality component in accordance with these periods as they ensue, and as and when the various qualities are available.

In blending tea the different components are chosen for their contribution to a number of desirable qualities in the brew such as colour, strength, pungency and flavour. In a branded blend price stability is essential and the greater part of any blended tea consists of tea of good average characteristics but without outstanding quality. The appearance of the dry leaf has also to be taken into consideration because certain specialized markets require teas of a particular type. Some markets such as the United Kingdom more readily absorb small teas, others the larger leaf grades. Profusion of tip is another specialized characteristic. Blackness and a good twist are more desirable than a brown stalky appearance or a flaky consistency. Too great a disparity in the particle size of individual components makes blending more difficult because of the settling out of the various grades of particle as they revolve in the large blending drums. The determination of the apparent specific gravity of a blend is a routine procedure in blending operations. Teas of low specific

65. Automatic weighing and filling machine for tea packets

66. Tea-tasting

67. Making and filling branded packets in a packing factory

gravity occupy a greater volume per unit weight and introduce difficulties into packeting in containers of uniform size.

Domestic water supplies differ in their mineral content according to the geological formations of the watersheds in which the supplies are collected and stored. Hard or chalybeate waters discolour the liquors and affect the soluble content of the tea extract. All these factors have to be considered in blending teas for sale in different localities.

The prescription for a blend is based on the tea-taster's reports on various teas. There are no quantitatively precise methods of evaluating quality, and consequently tea-tasting remains an art rather than a science. The concerted opinion of a panel of tea-tasters provides a reliable evaluation of a tea's worth. The tea-taster's verdict is valuable not only to the trade but to the research institutes in comparing the merits of different manufacturing methods.

TEA-TASTING

The technique of tea-tasting conforms to a standard procedure that ensures that comparisons made between various samples are valid. For this purpose a batch of tea samples is laid out and from each one a liquor is prepared. The taster's apparatus consists of a porcelain lipped cup fitted with a lid. The cup is of standard size and when full holds 140 ml. or a quarter of a pint. The weight of tea infused in each cup is traditionally that of a sixpenny piece (2·8 gms. or 44 grains) which amounts to a 2 per cent brew. The brew is timed with a six-minute sand-glass or alarum clock and the liquors are then poured off into a porcelain bowl. The infused leaf is then shaken on to the lid, by inverting the cup, pressed free of excess moisture and the reversed lid is replaced on the cup. For valuation and auction purposes the liquors are tasted without milk. On the other hand blenders use milk and larger pots which require a brew longer than six minutes.

In assessing the characteristics of a tea, the taster first examines the dry tea for colour, uniformity, twist, tip and aroma and then passes on to the infused leaf which rather confusingly he refers to as the "infusion." Ideally this should be a bright copper colour and substantially devoid of the green tinge of unchanged chlorophyll. From the colour and evenness of the infusion the taster forms his opinion of the nature, satisfactory or otherwise, of the fermentation. Removing the lid, he judges the aroma of the vapours confined in the cup. Whilst the extract is still warm the quality of liquors is judged first of all by assessing their appearance and then their taste. Liquors should be bright and clear when first poured, with a distinct reddish tinge that gives a faint pink meniscus where the liquor touches the bowl. When cool a good liquor becomes opaque owing to "creaming down," i.e. the precipitation from the solution of those compounds, referred to in Chapter XII, which are predominatingly ethyl acetate soluble fractions, derived from the oxidized and condensed polyphenols in association with caffeine.

In tasting, the liquors are drawn into the mouth by an inward breath rather than being merely sipped. This brings them into intimate contact with the tongue, palate and walls of the buccal cavity, which are physiologically sensitive to the flavour, strength and astringency of the liquid. The liquor is not swallowed but is expectorated into a spittoon.

The recognized features of a tea-taster's report relate to appearance, colour, strength, pungency and flavour, and all these are described in specialized terms. There are many synonyms and it would serve no useful purpose in a work of this nature to attempt to include even a major portion of them. The following represent those in common use and are listed as an indication of the characteristics that are consistently brought under review when tea-tasting is in progress. Self-explanatory terms are omitted except when it is desirable to indicate the cause of the characteristic they describe.

TEA-TASTING TERMS[5]

RELATIVE TO DRY LEAF

BLISTERED. With raised blisters on the surface due to firing at too high a temperature initially. This characteristic has no connection with blister blight.

BOLD. Too large for the specified grade.

CHOPPY. Subject to too much cutting in the dry condition.

CLEAN. Free from dust, stalk, fibre, etc.

EVEN. Homogeneous in particle size and conforming to the grade specification (cf. uneven).

FLAKY. Flat open leaf without twist and indicative of faulty withering, rolling or plucking, or a combination of these.

GRAINY. *See* SHOTTY.

GREY. Grey teas are produced by excessive handling and cutting in the sorting process.

SHOTTY. Small tightly twisted particles rather like grapenuts, usually associated with pekoe grades. When applied to fannings the alternative term grainy is used.

TIPPY. Showing a high percentage of tip, i.e. the extremity of the buds. Golden tips are desirable features for certain markets: silver tip indicates over-withering or damage during sorting.

RELATIVE TO INFUSED LEAF

BRIGHT. Used to describe colour that is uniform and of a reddish tinge.

COPPERY. A specially desirable variant of the former.

DULL. The antithesis of bright in the sense defined.

GREEN. The result of underfermentation.

MIXED. Containing leaf of diverse colours, red, green and dark brown: ascribable to uneven withering and fermentation.

RELATIVE TO LIQUORS

BRISK. Lively on the palate with some degree of pungency: usually associated with a satisfactorily fired tea.

BRIGHT. Indicative of clarity and brightness of the liquor.

DULL. The antithesis of the former.

FLAT. Lacking pungency and flavour, usually due to deterioration.

HARSH, RAW, RASPING. Bitter, due to the presence of unfermented polyphenols; a common defect of non-wither teas.

PLAIN. Lacking in the accepted desirable characteristics particularly pungency and quality.

PUNGENT. Astringent without bitterness.

QUALITY. A general integration of desirable characteristics.

ROUND or FULL. Satisfactory in strength and colour without harshness.

SMOOTH. Similar to the preceding but less pronounced.

SOFT. Antithesis of brisk and indicating a badly fired tea.

GENERAL TERMS

HIGH-FIRED. Fired at a high exhaust temperature but without burning: is not regarded as an entirely derogatory characteristic.

GONE-OFF. Deteriorated usually on account of high moisture content conducive to mouldiness.

MALTY. With a faint aroma of malt: a desirable feature associated with good firing in quality teas.

TAINTED. Contaminated with an extraneous flavour and aroma.

STANDARDS OF PURITY

The tea expert and taster are concerned with the commercial quality of the tea that passes through their hands and the criteria they use are based on the assumption that the teas examined are normal products of straightforward manufacture. A tea so badly made as to reveal a disregard of the principles of hygiene that have been previously described, would be recognized by them and would be appropriately discounted in value. The question of deliberate adulteration of tea by other substances, or of tea deemed unfit for human consumption, presents problems outside their normal range of experience and competence.

In England the sale of teas unfit for human consumption is prohibited under the terms of the Customs and Excise Act 1952: Section 229, Subsections 1 and 3. These sections read as follows:

(1) A sample of any tea imported as merchandise and unloaded in the United Kingdom may be taken and analysed by any person appointed in that behalf by the Commissioners and:

(a) if upon analysis of any sample so taken the tea is found to be mixed with any other substance or exhausted tea, it shall not be delivered from customs charge for any purpose without the sanction of the Commissioners; and

(b) if upon analysis as aforesaid the tea appears in the opinion of the analyst to be unfit for human consumption, the tea shall be deemed to have been condemned as forfeited under this act.

(3) In this section the expression "exhausted tea" means tea which has been deprived of its proper quality, strength or virtue by steeping, infusion, decoction or other means.

No prescribed tests or precise analytical limits are laid down in the Act and discretion is vested in the Customs Officials and the Government Chemist. Examination is not concerned with quality in the trade sense but with purity and fitness for consumption. Adulteration with spent tea-leaves or with leaves of other plants would be deemed to infringe regulations. A poor fibrous tea would not infringe the Act if the fibre was from tea stalk, even though to the trade the amount appeared excessive.

In Ceylon and India definite criteria are laid down in the Food and Drugs Act (Tea Regulations, 1952) and the Prevention of Food Adulteration Act, 1954, respectively. These relate to limits of ash content (4–7 per cent Ceylon; 5–8 per cent India) and the portion thereof soluble in water and hydrochloric acid; and to the percentage of extractable material when tea is refluxed for an hour with water. In both countries the minimum is 30 per cent. Ceylon stipulates that the copper content should not exceed 150 p.p.m. whilst India imposes a tolerance limit of 50 per cent for stalk. The weakness of these regulations is that they do not clearly distinguish between a tea that is adulterated and one which is merely a poor specimen.

THE TEA REGULATION SCHEME

The tea market has from time to time suffered from serious and prolonged slumps. In the early days of the plantation industry they originated in the extension of acreage and production at a pace that outstripped that of consumption. After the First World War accumulated stocks were indiscriminatingly released by the U.K. Government with consequent disorganization of the market and a severe drop in prices.

In 1930 India, Ceylon and the Netherlands East Indies inaugurated a scheme of voluntary restriction of exports, but this lasted for only a year and was not successful in rectifying the instability of prices. By 1933 the position had become more serious and a more comprehensive scheme was started under the auspices of a central organization, the International Tea Committee. In the first instance the agreement was negotiated solely by associations of tea producers in the respective countries, or their representatives in London. Eventually the scheme received the support of the Governments in the three countries, which enacted legislation to enforce the agreement. At the same time official representatives took their place on the Committee.

The basis of the agreement was that for a particular period the export quota should be fixed for each country at a percentage of the standard production of that country. Standard production was the maximum export figure for any of the years 1929–31 inclusive. Internal allocation of quotas to individual producers was relegated to the authorities in the countries concerned. The agreement also prohibited the planting of new acreages except with the permission of the controlling authority. These new acreages were intended to meet the needs of producers who, at the time the ban was imposed, had not an economic unit. Tea Research Institutes were exempt from the provisions of the agreement. In addition the supply of planting material to non-participants was prohibited.

The original agreement ratified by India, Ceylon and the Netherlands East Indies was planned to operate for five years with provision for renewal for further and similar periods. The second period 1938–43 was extended, owing to war conditions, till 1948. During this period East Africa and the then Nyasaland government joined the scheme but subsequently withdrew because they looked forward to the possibilities of substantial expansion. Malaya also observed the scheme's restriction of acreage, but not that of the exportable quota. These withdrawals led to long-drawn-out negotiations for the continuation of the scheme. Eventually the agreement, which at that time embraced India, Pakistan, Ceylon and Indonesia, was maintained till 1955, since when it has been in abeyance.

The International Tea Committee has, however, remained in being and fulfils a very valuable function in compiling statistics of tea production and trade.[2, 3] In this diminished role it receives the support of African producers.

TEA MARKET EXPANSION

Although the first objective of the International Tea Committee was to balance production and consumption by restriction of exports, the Committee was active from an early date in promoting agencies for publicity and propaganda directed towards tea market expansion. Prior to the establishment of the International Tea Committee the main producing countries had organized their own publicity which was supported by the imposition of a cess on exports. In 1935 the Committee sponsored the foundation of the International Tea Market Expansion Board whose function was to conduct publicity campaigns outside the countries of production.

The International Tea Market Expansion Board conducted publicity campaigns irrespective of sectional interests, but the secessions from the International Tea Committee had similar repercussions on the propaganda scheme also.

Since 1932 Ceylon has had a very active Statutory Tea Propaganda Board. The International Tea Market Expansion Board has now become the executive agent of the Ceylon Board in the importing countries. In the United Kingdom, United Arab Republic (Egypt), Iraq, Republic of South Africa, Denmark and Italy, Tea Bureaux for educational and propaganda purposes have been set up under the immediate control of the I.T.M.E.B. In the United States, Canada, Germany (West) and Australia it is in liaison with nationally constituted Tea Councils which is actively supports.[4]

MISCELLANEOUS ORGANIZATIONS

In addition to international agencies for the regulation and administration of the tea industry there are numerous organizations, sectional in character, concerned with the co-ordination of the large number of companies and estates that are active in tea production and marketing. There are broadly speaking three types of agency. The first is purely mercantile. Most tea companies employ agency houses to carry out the routine business of their directorates. These agencies arrange for storage and shipment of teas; for purchase and supply of equipment and for supervision of staff. They retain "visiting agents" to report periodically on the work and condition of estates and to advise on matters of policy. In some instances they are implicated in the financial affairs of the companies whose agents they are. A typical agency house performs its functions on behalf of a number of individual estates and companies.

In producing countries there are also voluntary associations which deliberate on matters of common interest to all members and are able to represent the views of the whole industry, or a particular sector of it, to the general public and, in particular, to ministerial and other government departments. These associations are autonomous and non-political but their views are of considerable importance to governments in planning the country's economic projects. The nature and purpose of these associations is well illustrated by recording the names of the best established of those wholly or significantly concerned with tea.

In India the predominant bodies are the Indian Tea Association; the United Planters Association of Southern India; the Calcutta Tea Traders Association and the Calcutta Tea Merchants Association. Ceylon has its century-old Planters Association of Ceylon and the Colombo Tea Traders Association. In Malaya the Incorporated Society of Planters serves both rubber and tea interests. Indonesia has its Algemeen Landbouw Syndicat (General Agricultural Syndicate) and the Zuid-en-West-Sumatra Syndicat (S. and W. Sumatra Syndicate). In Africa the East African Tea Traders Association, the Tea Association of Central Africa, the Kenya Tea Growers Association and the Tea Associations of Uganda and Tanganyika respectively are of a similar nature to their counterparts elsewhere.

London, as the oldest tea market, has representative associations connected with all branches of the trade and industry. Their variety and function are shown by the membership of the Tea Trade Committee on which the ancillary associations are represented. These are:

The Indian Tea Association (London).
The Pakistan Tea Association.
The South Indian Association in London.
The Ceylon Association in London.
The Indonesian Association (Incorporated).
The Tea Association of Central Africa (London Committee).
The Tea Boards of Kenya, Uganda and Tanganyika.
The Tea Brokers Association of London.
The Tea Buying Brokers Association of London.
The Tea Buyers Association.
The Tea Clearing House.

Planned economies have led in post-war years to considerable intervention by governments into the affairs of the industry, apart from imposing taxation in support of revenue. India, Pakistan,

Kenya, Uganda and Tanganyika have statutory Tea Boards on which both government and the industry are represented. Similar functions are exercised in Ceylon by the Tea Controller. The powers of these boards vary and are set out in the ordinances setting them up, but in general the range of control includes licensing of land for tea cultivation, licensing of brokers and selling agencies, local price fixation and export quotas.

TEA RESEARCH

The need for, and the benefits derived from, agricultural research are now taken for granted, and the present century has seen the establishment of a great variety of research institutes of both a general and a specialized nature. Amongst these are a number of commodity research institutes devoting their attention to individual crops. The tea industry was in the van of this movement. Whilst acknowledging the help given them by colonial Agricultural Departments, the various sections of the tea-producing industry, situate in their several countries and localities, have demanded more detailed and specialized help than official departments have been able to provide. Consequently they have to a considerable extent organized, financed, and controlled their own research facilities. The chief of these research centres are the following:

PROEFSTATION VOOR THEE
(Tea Experimental Station)
Buitenzorg, Java, Indonesia

This is the oldest establishment of its kind. In 1893 the Soeka-boemische Landbouwvereniging, an agricultural association founded to promote the cultivation of tea, sponsored the appointment of a tea officer to work at the Buitenzorg Botanic Gardens. In 1902 a special substation for tea was opened which was replaced in 1927 by new headquarters. Till 1925 the research funds were contributed by a minority of individual estates. Thereafter the Algemeen Landbouw Syndicat (General Agricultural Syndicate), an amalgamation of existing agricultural associations, took over financial control. During the slump of the early 'thirties the membership of the syndicate diminished to a degree that threatened the financial stability of the research station, and in 1933 control was vested in a government organization the Centrale Vereniging tot beheer van Proefstations voor de overjarige cultures (Central Organization for the management of Experimental Stations for perennial crops). The payment of a subvention for research then became compulsory for all estates.

The official connection has continued since the establishment of the Indonesian Republic.

The Proefstation is prominently associated with the earliest work on selection of improved types of tea and on the chemical composition of tea leaf.

The publications of the Proefstation are occasional. Early issues consisted of the *Mededeelingen van het Proefstation voor Thee*. These gave place in 1933 to the *Archief voor de Thee Cultuur*. In addition, from 1920–26 a quarterly journal *De Thee* was in existence.

The Proefstation voor Thee is now incorporated into the Proefstation West Java.

THE INDIAN TEA ASSOCIATION SCIENTIFIC DEPARTMENT

Tocklai Experimental Station, Cinnamara, Assam

This station is a private institution in the sense that it serves the needs of the Indian Tea Association only, but as the great majority of tea producers in North-east India are members of the Association its work is available to most estates in Assam and West Bengal. The inauguration of the station dates back to 1900 when a laboratory was opened in the Indian Museum, Calcutta. In 1904 an entomological laboratory was started at Kannykoorie, Cachar, followed later by a chemical laboratory at Heeleaka in Assam, close to the present headquarters. The Tocklai Station was opened in 1912 and replaced the existing laboratories. In addition to laboratories the station has 100 acres of land and an experimental factory close by at Borbhetta.

The affairs of the station are governed by a Scientific Department Sub-committee of the parent association. The parent association supplies all funds except those derived from a small government grant.

Tocklai publishes an annual report and a monthly news letter. In addition, as occasional publications, there are proceedings of conferences, memoranda on specific subjects and a Tea Encyclopedia which is constantly revised by the issue of recensions of former contributions.

The station is specially noted for long-term investigations into the physiology of the tea bush and the fundamental chemistry of the tea leaf. Of recent years it has inaugurated an Engineering Development Branch for the study of design in tea machinery. By constructing and testing prototypes that incorporate new conceptions, it is making a significant contribution to the integration of the various processes involved in manufacture into a continuous automotive operation.

PAKISTAN TEA RESEARCH STATION

Srimangal, Sylhet, E. Pakistan

The partition involved in Indo-Pakistan independence in 1947 cut off tea estates in parts of the Surmah Valley and Chittagong from the services of the Tocklai Experimental Station. In 1952 the Pakistan Tea Board took steps to establish and finance its own tea research station which commenced active investigations in 1958.

Research, in its early stages, is concerned with soil surveys of prospective new areas; improvement in fertilizer practices; irrigation; clonal selection and propagation and the control of pests, diseases and weeds. Field investigations are carried out on the Station's estate and in co-operation with commercial estates, for whom an advisory service is provided.

The Station publishes a Report (biennial); *The Tea Journal of Pakistan* (twice yearly), and from time to time circulars and pamphlets on specific and topical subjects.

TEA RESEARCH INSTITUTE OF CEYLON

Talawakelle

The Ceylon institute was founded in 1925 at the instigation of the Planters Association of Ceylon with the co-operation of the then existing Ceylon Estates Proprietary Association and the Ceylon Association in London. These associations procured the enactment of a Tea Research Ordinance that provided for an autonomous Board of Management on which the major agricultural associations were represented. Additional members were nominated to represent government and smallholders. Funds are raised by an export cess on tea collected by the Customs Authorities. All estates and smallholders are beneficiaries of the scheme, and all ordinary revenue comes from the industry itself. The only contribution from general revenue has been a block grant-in-aid for research on blister blight control.

The institute is unique in having a fully developed commercial estate of more than 400 acres of which 290 carry tea in bearing. The factory, which produces some 300,000 lb. of tea per annum, is provided with both commercial and pilot plant. A special Smallholdings Advisory Department catered for the needs of the 70,000 acres of tea smallholdings until the Department of Agriculture took it over in 1958.

The institute publishes an annual report; bulletins on specific subjects; a series of occasional monographs that from time to time integrate the results of investigations carried out over a considerable period of time; a series of technical pamphlets and a journal *The Tea Quarterly*. The work of the Institute covers a wide range of projects. Selection and vegetative propagation of clonal material has been a major commitment for many years. Tea technology maintains its prominence and has recently been active in working out a process for the manufacture of a tea extract from fermented leaf. On the biological side it has to its credit the successful control of blister blight, tea tortrix and shot-hole-borer.

UNITED PLANTERS ASSOCIATION OF SOUTH INDIA

(Scientific Department)

Coonoor

Since 1926 this association has maintained a small experimental station at Devarshola, Nilgiris. This station is now to be used as a substation to a larger experimental station with new laboratories situated in the Anamallais.

The station receives some financial assistance from Government. The Tea Section of the Scientific Department is mainly concerned with the control of pests and diseases and with general cultural problems. It publishes an annual report containing an appendix of technical papers on subjects under investigation, technical bulletins and also uses *The Planter's Chronicle*, the official organ of U.P.A.S.I., as a medium for occasional publication.

THE TEA RESEARCH STATION

Mimosa, Mlanje, Malawi

This station and its substation at Cholo, formerly under the control of the Department of Agriculture in colonial Nyasaland, are now in the charge of the Tea Association of Central Africa which serves Rhodesia as well as Malawi. The experimental stations still work in close association with, and receive specialist help from, the Malawi Department of Agriculture.

In addition to general agronomic investigations, a prominent research project is concerned with climatological studies in relation to soil-moisture reserves and the physiological needs of the tea plant. In association with the School of Biochemistry at Cambridge University, investigations into the mechanism of fermentation have been prosecuted. The stations publish an annual report and a quarterly news letter.

THE TEA RESEARCH INSTITUTE OF EAST AFRICA

Kericho, Kenya

Inaugurated in 1949 under the sponsorship of African Tea Holdings Ltd. (now Brooke Bond East Africa Ltd.), the Institute was incorporated in 1951 as a company limited by guarantee without share capital. The autonomous governing body includes representatives of the statutory Tea Boards of each territory, the Departments of Agriculture and the East Africa Common Services Organization.

The activities of the Institute range over a variety of climatic and edaphic conditions. In addition to the central research station and estate at Kericho, the Institute has two substations, one in the Toro district of the Western Province of Uganda, and the other at Amani, Tanganyika. Supplementary to the field experiments at the stations there is a comprehensive network of statistically controlled field trials on company estates. The Institute maintains a close liaison with the Kenya Tea Development Authority which is concerned with the development of African-grown tea. Vegetative propagation and the biology of *Armillaria mellea* are major subjects under investigation.

REFERENCES

1. The Monopolies and Restrictive Practices Commission. *Report on the Supply of Tea*, H.M.S.O., London, 1956.
2. MORRISON, R. D., *Memorandum Relating to the Tea Industry and Tea Trade of the World*, International Tea Committee, 1943.
3. International Tea Committee, *Bulletin of Statistics* (twice yearly). London.
4. Ceylon Tea Propaganda Board Report, Colombo, 1963.
5. HARLER, C. R., *The Culture and Marketing of Tea*, 3rd edn., O.U.P., 1964.

Chapter XV

STATISTICAL REVIEW

Acreage and Production—Consumption—Distribution.

THE presentation of data showing the production of tea on a global basis is hampered by a number of circumstances. Until the International Tea Committee's records were published, no collated statistics of tea production, consumption and distribution were available. The number and diversity of productive units are great. In some of the major tea-producing countries their size varies from a fraction of an acre to several thousands. At the present time smallholdings are on the increase, especially in Africa, where the encouragement of peasant holdings is a matter of Government policy in the newly independent countries. Political factors obtrude in some instances. It is still impossible to get official figures from China, and only in the last few years have data from the U.S.S.R. been released.

In a work such as this great detail is neither possible nor desirable. It must suffice therefore to present the main data and point out the trends that seem to be significant, always remembering that current statistics can become out-of-date in a remarkably short time.

ACREAGE AND PRODUCTION

The table Appendix I gives the acreage and production figures published by the International Tea Committee, supplemented to a small degree by national figures where these are more recent.[1, 2] The tea industry has settled down to a considerable degree into a recognizable postwar pattern, and at this distance of time comparisons with prewar figures are academic. The effects of the Second World War are not entirely obliterated. Indonesia for example has not built up its acreage to prewar levels, the non-peasant area being only a little more than half its former size. Between 1955 and 1962 there has been a slight fall and this probably indicates that no expansion is contemplated. An important aspect of recent statistics is that since 1955 the International Tea Agreement has been inoperative. Production is now unrestricted and the figures reflect more factually the capacity of the industry in its several regions.

189

Percentage Changes in Acreages and Production, 1955–62

	Acreage	Production
India	+4	+12·5
Pakistan	+7	−2
Ceylon	+4	+23
Indonesia	−2·5	+10
Japan	+28	+6
Formosa	−19	+33
East Africa	+93	+96
Malawi	+18	+60
Mozambique	+26	+60
U.S.S.R.	—	+47

The countries listed in the International Tea Committee's Bulletin of Statistics show an average increase in production of over 20 per cent, to which a small rise of 6 per cent in acreage contributes. Undoubtedly the main factor has been increase in yield per acre. From region to region the variation is marked, and only close association with the individual countries can elucidate the reasons for the variability shown in the table. Seasonal influences have to be taken into account but in most instances progress has been steady. East Africa shows the largest gain both in area and production, but because new and temporarily unproductive areas are a constant component of the acreage figures the rise in production does no more than keep pace with the increment of area. Old-established regions, where there is little expansion of acreage, show increased productivity far ahead of what can be attributed to increment of area. In India, Ceylon, Mozambique and Malawi this development stems from better cultural practices. These countries have well-established and active research stations. There is probably no branch of agricultural industry where closer links exist between science and practice than in the tea industry. An abundance of experimental evidence is now available showing that properly conceived manurial programmes can increase yields without damaging quality if facilities for manufacture keep pace with increase of crop. Consequently much higher targets for yield per acre are now accepted as both reasonable and desirable.

Apart from political intervention into the affairs of the tea in-dustry there are three factors which may be expected to play a major part in determining the productivity of the industry. The first is the planting, or replanting in most instances, of a considerable acreage with clonal stock of high potential yield. So far the level of achieve-ment in this direction has been very modest indeed. Because of this, the second factor that becomes of distinct importance is the yield potential of existing acreages during, say, the next generation. Can these acres of old tea be kept at the present level of yield until clonal stocks take over? The yield curves in Chapter VIII indicate that even if the ceiling of yield per acre is still some way off, the now customarily high rates of fertilizer application are operating in the region where further increments of yield may be possible only at extravagant costs. It would be idle to deny that there are large areas of tea that will not respond satisfactorily to the stock panacea of more nutrient. Can they be kept in a reasonable state of production for the period envisaged?

Agriculturally these questions can be answered in the affirmative. The overriding factor is cost balanced against the state of the market which nobody can predict. Will tea prices remain sufficiently high to bear the burden of increasing costs of production or the capital costs of replanting? It may well be that the future prosperity of the industry lies in maintaining smaller acreages with less overhead costs, higher yields and lower costs of production. A precedent for this policy can be found in the replanting programmes in Assam during the nineteen-thirties where, making use of better jats, production was concentrated near the factory and outlying gardens were discarded.

CONSUMPTION

The probability of increased yields will be of no avail unless the demand for tea keeps pace with the supply. The table Appendix II shows how and where consumption has increased in various parts of the world, over a period of seven years.

The United Kingdom shows a 10 per cent increase which cannot be regarded as significant since fluctuations are frequent and it is well below the maximum attained in 1957, viz. 558 million lb.

Europe as a whole shows an increase after allowing for the U.S.S.R. figures now available. The same is true of every continental region where in non-producing countries increases range from 16 to 25 per cent. The most notable increases, proportionally, are in Ceylon 73 per cent and Indonesia 64 per cent, but they are small consumers and these high figures are less important than that for the Indian sub-continent with a figure of 31 per cent. The home consumption is thus almost 42 per cent of the production in 1962. This is an approximate figure because, being based upon a particular year, it takes no account of fluidity of stocks.

The figures for *per capita* consumption of tea show how firmly tea drinking is established wherever British people make their homes. Outside the British Isles the rest of the continent of Europe makes very sparing use of the beverage. Only Iraq rivals the Commonwealth in the tea-drinking habit. The estimated consumptions per person in pounds are:

United Kingdom	.. 9·6	Netherlands	.. 1·6
Eire	.. 9·4	Chile	.. 1·5
Australia ..	.. 5·9	Malaya	.. 0·5
New Zealand ..	.. 7·2	Sudan	.. 1·4
Iraq	.. 7·5	Tunisia	.. 2·3
Ceylon ..	.. 4·1	Iran	.. 1·9
Canada ..	.. 2·5	Japan	.. 1·8
Egypt	.. 2·3	Algeria	.. 0·8
Morocco ..	.. 2·6	U.S.A.	.. 0·7
Republic of South Africa..	2·1	India	.. 0·7

DISTRIBUTION

Political and trade affiliations play a considerable part in determining the destinations to which the chief producers export their tea. Sterling bloc countries tend to trade with others in the same group, and, as the United Kingdom is in addition a high consumer, all major producers export tea to this country. For tea producers within the Commonwealth the United Kingdom provides the predominating market. Appendix III gives each producer's principal consumers.

Propinquity of markets is a further factor influencing exports. Instances of this operative over a long period are the relations between Indonesia and Malaya; Uganda and the Sudan; Mozambique and South Africa; Formosa and Hong Kong. Even longstanding relations are apt to be disturbed by political events. No Indonesian tea exports to the Netherlands are recorded since 1959, Belgium and Iraq taking their place, whilst those to Malaya are now in jeopardy. Similarly exports from Mozambique to South Africa have decreased almost to vanishing point. Only the United Kingdom appears to be increasing its trade with this country.

Finally, specialized requirements are a consideration: the green teas of Japan and Formosa are a particular feature of exports to Morocco and Algeria.

REFERENCES

1. International Tea Committee, *Bulletin of Statistics* (twice annually). London. Government Press, Colombo, 1952.
2. J. H. Thomas and Co. Private Ltd., Calcutta, Statistics, 1964.

Appendix I

ACREAGE (thousands) AND PRODUCTION (million lb.)

	1955		1962	
	Acreage	Production	Acreage	Production
N. India	616	543	641	579
S. India	176	135	184	185
Pakistan	75	52	80*	51
Ceylon	566	380	591	467
Indonesia	198	85	193	94
Vietnam	13	5·8	23	10
Malaysia	8·4	5·3	8·6	6·2
Formosa	116	30	93	40
Japan	95	161	122	171
Kenya	25	19	49	36
Uganda	10	7	21	14
Tanganyika	11·5	4·5	20	10
Malawi	26	18	31	29
Rhodesia	2·1	1·0	5·6	2·8
Mozambique	30	13	38	21
Mauritius	2·9	1·3	4·5	2·8
Turkey	18	2·7	38	18
U.S.S.R.	163	62	163	91
Argentina	80	4	62	22

*1961

193

Appendix II

CONSUMPTION (million lb.) NON-PRODUCING COUNTRIES

		1955	1962
U.K.	.. ..	464	510
Eire	.. ..	26	24
Netherlands	..	16	19
U.S.S.R.	.. ..	—	27
Other Europe	..	31	59
	Total	537	639
U.S.A.	.. ..	104	129
Canada	.. ..	42	40
Other America	..	12	21
	Total	158	190
Arabia	.. ..	15	18
Iran	.. ..	22	14
Iraq	.. ..	29	44
Other Asia ..	..	44	61
	Total	110	137
Egypt	.. ..	38	59
N. Africa	..	48	44
S. Africa	.. ..	23	30
Sudan	.. ..	16	19
Other Africa..	..	19	26
	Total	144	178
Australia	.. ..	54	61
New Zealand	..	13	17
	Total	67	78

CONSUMPTION OF PRODUCING COUNTRIES

		1955	1962
India and Pakistan	..	261	342
Ceylon	.. ..	15	26
Indonesia	.. ..	22	36
E. Africa	.. ..	9	11

194

Appendix III

PRINCIPAL CUSTOMERS OF MAIN EXPORTING COUNTRIES
(1962 unless otherwise stated)

Data in Millions of Pounds

INDIA		CEYLON		INDONESIA (1961)	
U.K.	.. 258	U.K.	.. 174	Netherlands	Nil
U.S.A.	.. 22	Australia	.. 38	Malaya	.. 6
Eire	.. 15	U.S.A.	.. 42	U.K.	.. 22
Canada	.. 12	Iraq	.. 43	U.S.A.	.. 8
Egypt	.. 42	Egypt	.. 6	Australia	.. 12
Iran	.. 5	S. Africa	.. 30	Germany	.. 8
Australia	.. 8	N. Zealand	.. 17	Belgium	.. 12
Turkey	.. 1				

KENYA		UGANDA		TANGANYIKA	
U.K.	.. 19·6	U.K.	.. 5·1	U.K.	.. 7·0
U.S.A.	.. 4·1	Sudan	.. 1·5	U.S.A.	.. 0·6
Sudan	.. 1·2	U.S.A.	.. 1·3	Canada	.. 0·4
Canada	.. 2·2	Canada	.. 1·1		
S. Africa	.. 0·9				

MOZAMBIQUE (1963)		MALAWI	
U.K.	.. 12·9	U.K.	.. 18
U.S.A.	.. 1·3		

JAPAN		FORMOSA	
Algeria	.. 3·9	Hong Kong	.. 2·4
U.K.	.. 0·6	U.K.	.. 0·8
U.S.A.	.. 2·4	U.S.A.	.. 6·7
Morocco	.. 5·5	Morocco	.. 7·5
		Thailand	.. 1·5

195

INDEX

Acaphylla theae, 127
Acreage under tea, 193
Adulteration, 17, 180
Africa, contrasting methods, 67, 156; soils, 68
Aglaospora aculeata, 116
Agrotype, 16, 93
Albizzia, 12
  chinensis, 89, 92
  gummifera, 91
  moluccana, 88
  odoratissima, 88
  stipulata, 88
Albizzia, manurial value of, 92
Aluminium, 138; accumulation in tea, 11; availability, 11; in relation to iron, 11; in relation to pH, 11; indicator plants, 12
Amani (Tanganyika), 3
Ambrosial fungus, 129
Amino-acids, in leaf, 140; related to quality, 140
Ammonium chloride, 84
Ammonium nitrate, 77, 84
Ammonium sulphate, 77, 84, 101
Ammonium sulphate—nitrate, 84
Anthocyanins, 143
Apical growth, producing leading shoots, 20
Arabinose, in leaf, 140
Arable agriculture, ecology of, 64; disturbance due to, 64, 65; tea as subject of, 65
Archaic rocks, 8
Argentine, 4
Armillaria mellea, control, 104; elimination of, 105; incidence of, 98, 105
Aroma, 158, 177; amino-acids related to, 140
Artificial Manures, soil fertility effects, 86. (*See also* Manures)

Ascorbic acid, 144
Assam: bheti planting in, 29; bush formation, 45; disease incidence, 97, 98; establishment of tea, 2, 3; factory hygiene, 164; jats, 15; pink mite confined to, 127; plucking standards, 59; pruning, 53-7; quality periods, 147; research, 97, 185; rolling procedure, 156, 157; seed bearers, 23, 24; shade, 89-93; soils, 8, 12; *Tephrosia*, use of, 28, 95; winter planting, 27, 43, 44, 51
Australia, 4

Bacteria on tea leaf, 149, 154; quality affected by, 149, 159
"Ball" planting, 29
Banjhi, periodic phases, 19, 20
Battens, 155, 156
Belippa sp., 122
Benzoquinone (ortho), 143
"Bheel" soils, 13
"Bheti" plants, 29
"Big Bulk", criterion of manufacture, 157
"Bitten-off" Disease, 99
Black Root Disease, 107
Black Rot Disease, 113
Blending, 176; problems involved in, 176
Blister Blight, 109; spread of, 97, 98; sunshine control, 111
Blood Meal, 77
Bolivia, 4
Bone Meal, 84
Botanic Gardens: Calcutta, 2; Durban, 3
Botanical characters of tea, 15
Botryodiplodia theobromae, 108
Bracken, as plant indicator, 12
Brahmaputra Valley, soils of, 8, 9